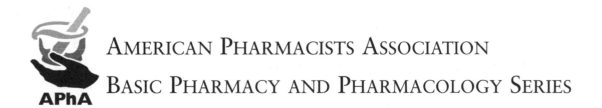

AMERICAN PHARMACISTS ASSOCIATION
BASIC PHARMACY AND PHARMACOLOGY SERIES

The Pharmacy Technician

WORKBOOK AND CERTIFICATION REVIEW

-FOURTH EDITION-

PERSPECTIVE PRESS
MORTON PUBLISHING COMPANY
www.morton-pub.com

Morton Publishing

Printed in the United States of America.

Morton Publishing Company
925 West Kenyon Avenue, Unit 12
Englewood, CO 80110
phone: 1-303-761-4805
fax: 1-303-762-9923
www.morton-pub.com

International Standard Book Number
ISBN 10: 0-89582-829-4
ISBN 13: 978-89582-829-3

10 9 8 7 6 5 4 3 2 1

Library of Congress Control Number: 2009926154

Cover photo credit: ©iStockphoto.com/Steve Cole, christie and cole studio inc.

NOTICE

To the best of the Publisher's knowledge, the information presented in this book follows general practice as well as federal and state regulations and guidelines. However, please note that you are responsible for following your employer's and your state's policies and guidelines.

The job description for pharmacy technicians varies by institution and state. Your employer and state can provide you with the most recent regulations, guidelines, and practices that apply to your work.

The Publisher of this book disclaims any responsibility whatsoever for any injuries, damages, or other conditions that result from your practice of the skills described in this book for any reason whatsoever.

THE PHARMACY TECHNICIAN

WORKBOOK AND

CERTIFICATION REVIEW

FOURTH EDITION

TABLE OF CONTENTS

TABLE OF CONTENTS

TABLE OF CONTENTS

PREFACE

THIS WORKBOOK

This workbook was developed to correspond with the textbook, *The Pharmacy Technician* by Perspective Press. For pharmacy technician students, it is a valuable tool for success in your training course. It provides a useful format for memorizing important information and for checking your knowledge of it. Key concepts and terms are carefully explained, and there are over 1000 exercises and problems to test your knowledge. Working these exercises out successfully will help you to succeed in your training.

It is important you follow through the workbook chapter by chapter and try answering the questions before looking up the answers. Once you have completed a chapter, review it and try to memorize the answers to the questions you missed.

A REVIEW GUIDE

The workbook can also be used as a review guide in preparing for the national Pharmacy Technician Certification Examination (PTCE) given by the Pharmacy Technician Certification Board (PTCB) or the Exam for the Certification of Pharmacy Technicians (ExCPT) given by ICPT. All its chapters are important in the taking either certification exam. However, special attention should be placed on Chapter 6—Calculations, as the exam will have calculation type problem solving that is often challenging for technicians taking the exam. The method used (ratio and proportion) in this section will solve any calculation problem you come across on the certification exams as well as most problems in the pharmacy setting. A careful review of this workbook will prepare you for much of either certification exam. However, some questions on the exams require knowledge gained from practice as a technician. Pharmacy technicians who have work experience in a pharmacy setting will therefore have an advantage in taking a certification exam. As an additional study tool, we have included two practice exams at the back of this book, one in the format of the PTCE and one in the format of ExCPT.

OVERVIEW: PHARMACY TECHNICIAN CERTIFICATION EXAM (PTCE)

The National Pharmacy Technician Certification Examination was established to allow the certification of technicians. The need for highly qualified pharmacy technicians is increasingly important as pharmacists are relinquishing many dispensing duties for more clinical ones, and the technician is playing a greater role.

Currently the national examination is given by the Pharmacy Technician Certification Board (PTCB) and applications are accepted continuously throughout the year. Applications are submitted online and applicants must take the exam within 90 days of submitting their application. The cost of taking this examination is at the time of this writing one-hundred and twenty-nine dollars.

THE PTCE EXAM

The examination contains 90 multiple choice questions. The multiple choice format involves four possible answers with only one answer being the best or most correct. The time limit for taking this examination is two hours. Exams are given in a Computer-Based Testing (CBT) format and each candidate is presented with different items.

SCORING OF THE PTCE EXAM

The scoring of the examination is based on the combined average of scores in three functional areas:

1. Assisting the Pharmacist in Serving Patients (66% of Exam)

   Includes activities related to traditional pharmacy prescription dispensing and medication distribution, and collecting and organizing information.

2. Maintaining Medication and Inventory Control Systems (22% of Exam)

   Includes activities related to medication and supply purchasing, inventory control, and preparation and distribution of medications according to approved policies and procedures.

3. Participating in the Administration and Management of Pharmacy Practice (12% of Exam)

   Includes activities related to the administrative process for the pharmacy practice center, including: operations, human resources, facilities and equipment, and information systems.

The combined score range of the exam is 300 to 900 points with a passing of 650 points required.

WHAT YOU NEED TO KNOW FOR THE PTCE EXAM

Specific information on examination content is provided in the PTCB's **Guidebook to Certification**, which can be downloaded from their site: www.ptcb.org.

For additional information, contact the PTCB at:

Pharmacy Technician Certification Board
2215 Constitution Avenue, NW
Washington, DC 20037-2985
800-363-8012 (phone)
202-429-7596 (fax)
www.ptcb.org

OVERVIEW: EXAM FOR THE CERTIFICATION OF PHARMACY TECHNICIANS (ExCPT)

The ExCPT is sponsored by the Institute for the Certification of Pharmacy Technicians (ICPT). The mission of the Institute for the Certification of Pharmacy Technicians is "to recognize pharmacy technicians who are proficient in the knowledge and skills needed to assist pharmacists to safely, accurately and efficiently prepare and dispense prescriptions and to promote high standards of practice for pharmacy technicians."

The exam is offered continuously, throughout the year at psi/LaserGrade testing centers. Candidates may register by calling the psi/LaserGrade toll-free number 1-800-211-2754 or they can identify testing center locations online at www.lasergrade.com. The cost of taking this examination is at the time of this writing one-hundred and five dollars.

THE ExCPT EXAM

The exam contains 110 multiple choice questions. The multiple choice format involves four possible answers with only one answer being the best or most correct. The time limit for taking this examination is two hours. Exams are given in a CBT format and each candidate is presented with different items.

SCORING OF THE ExCPT EXAM

ExCPT exam questions fall in three main areas:

1. Regulations and Technician Duties (~25% of exam)

2. Drugs and Drug Therapy (~23% of exam)

3. Dispensing Process (~52% of Exam)

Scoring for the ExCPT exam is established by the ICPT Expert Panel and uses the Angoff procedure to determine the passing score. The passing score is not based on a curve.

WHAT YOU NEED TO KNOW FOR THE ExCPT EXAM

Specific information on examination content is provided in the ExCPT Candidate's Guide which is available from their site: www.nationaltechexam/org.

For additional information, contact the ICPT at:

Institute for the Certification of Pharmacy Technicians
2536 S. Old Hwy 94
Suite 224
St. Charles, MO 63303
(314) 442-6775 (phone)
(866) 203-9213 (fax)

ACKNOWLEDGEMENTS

Mary F. Powers, Ph.D., R.Ph.

Mary Powers has been a key contributor on *The Pharmacy Technician*, on which this workbook is based, since the first edition. She was a key contributor to the first edition of *The Pharmacy Technician Workbook and Certification Review* and has been its sole author since the second edition. For the fourth edition of the workbook Mary collaborated with the publisher on a plan for the new edition, updated existing content to reflect changes made in the corresponding text, updated the PTCE Practice Exam, provided a new ExCPT Practice Exam, and provided the lists of the top 200 brand name drugs, top 200 generic drugs, and the top 200 brand name drugs by classification. Mary also answered questions and helped fine tune many aspects of both the main text and the workbook. An Associate Professor of Pharmacy Practice at the University of Toledo College of Pharmacy, Toledo, OH, Mary's input has always been enormously helpful, and we cannot thank her enough.

Others We'd Like To Thank

We would also like to acknowledge Joe Medina, CPhT, B.S. Pharmacy. Joe contributed to the first edition of this workbook by writing many of the exam review questions and other exercises. Joe has served as the Chairperson/Program Director for the Pharmacy Technician Programs at Front Range Community College and Arapahoe Community College in the Denver metro area.

In addition, this workbook would not have been possible without the efforts of a large number of people who worked on the corresponding text, *The Pharmacy Technician, Fourth Edition*. We would like to thank them again for their contributions. We couldn't have done it without their help:

Robert P. Shrewsbury, Ph.D., R.Ph., Associate Professor of Pharmaceutics, University of North Carolina-Chapel Hill; Brenda Vonderau, B.Sc. (Pharm.), Director, Medication Therapy Management Programs, Catalyst Rx; Cindy B. Johnson, R.Ph., L.C.S.W., RxMentor Pharmacist, Humana; Steve Johnson, BS., R.Ph., Meditech Lead Analyst, Catholic Health Initiatives; Ruth Duke, Pharm.D., Pharmacist, CVS Pharmacy; Pamela Nicoski, Pharm.D., Clinical Pharmacist, Loyola University Medical Center; Britta Penn, Pharm.D., Clinical Pharmacist, Children's Memorial Hospital; and Melanie V. Duhaine, R.N., B.S.N., M.Ed., Director of Nursing, Fairchild Manor, Senior-Associates of Western New York.

We are also grateful to several reviewers whose insights and feedback on previous editions helped shape the fourth edition: James Austin, Weatherford College; CVS Pharmacy; Marisa Fetzer, Institute of Technology; Claudia Johnson, Polytech Adult Education; Mary Anna Marshall, Virginia Pharmacists Association and Hanover High School; Tony David Ornelas; Peter E. Vonderau, Scolari's Food & Drug, Inc.; and Walgreen Co.

Finally, we would like to thank Tammy Newnam for preparing the art; Hannah Hogan for designing and preparing the cover; Patricia Billiot for proof-reading; Dona Mendoza, Carter Fenton, and Chrissy Morton of Morton Publishers for their help with the fourth edition; and Doug Morton, whose sponsorship makes this book possible.

Perspective Press

AMERICAN PHARMACISTS ASSOCIATION
BASIC PHARMACY AND PHARMACOLOGY SERIES

Dear Student or Instructor,

The American Pharmacists Association (APhA), the national professional society of pharmacists in the United States, and Morton Publishing Company, a publisher of educational texts and training materials in healthcare, are pleased to present this outstanding workbook, *Pharmacy Technician Workbook and Certification Review, Fourth Edition*. It is one of a series of distinctive texts and training materials for basic pharmacy and pharmacology training that is published under this banner: *American Pharmacists Association Basic Pharmacy and Pharmacology Series*.

Each book in the series is oriented toward developing an understanding of fundamental concepts. In addition, each text presents applied and practical information on the skills necessary to function effectively in the workplace. Each of the books in the series uses a visual design to enhance understanding and ease of use and is accompanied by various instructional support materials. We think you will find them valuable training tools.

The American Pharmacists Association and Morton Publishing thank you for using this book and invite you to look at other titles in this series, which are listed below.

Thomas E. Menighan, BSPharm, MBA
Executive Vice President
Chief Executive Officer
American Pharmacists Association

Douglas N. Morton
President
Morton Publishing Company

TITLES IN THIS SERIES:

The Pharmacy Technician, Fourth Edition
Pharmacy Technician Workbook and Certification Review, Fourth Edition

The Pharmacy Technician

WORKBOOK AND CERTIFICATION REVIEW

— 1 —

PHARMACY & HEALTH CARE

KEY CONCEPTS

Test your knowledge by covering the information in the right hand column.

pharmacology	The study of drugs, their properties, uses, application, and effects.
herbal medicine	People have used drugs derived from plants to treat illnesses and other physical conditions for thousands of years. The ancient Greeks used the bark of a white willow tree to relieve pain. The bark contained salicylic acid, the natural forerunner of the active ingredient in aspirin.
cocaine	The first effective local anesthetic.
digitalis	The drug of the foxglove plant which has been widely used in treating heart disease.
quinine	The first useful drug in the treatment of malaria, one of mankind's most deadly diseases. It was extracted from the bark of a Peruvian tree, the Cinchona.
germ theory	The theory that microorganisms cause food spoilage.
polio vaccine	The use of an injectable vaccine made from killed polio virus and an oral polio vaccine made from a weakened form of live polio virus was important to prevent the spread of this crippling and often fatal disease.
insulin	The hormone that lowers blood sugar in the treatment of diabetes—one of the great discoveries in medicine in the twentieth century.

penicillin	The first antibiotic.
average life span	This measure of health has increased by over twenty years in the United States in the Twentieth Century.
synthetic drugs	Drugs created by reformulating simpler chemicals into more complex ones, creating a new chemical not found in nature.
Human Genome Project	An attempt to map the entire DNA sequence in the human genome. This information will provide a better understanding of hereditary diseases and how to treat them.
pharmacist education and training	To become a pharmacist in the United States, an individual must have earned a Doctor of Pharmacy degree from an accredited college of pharmacy (of which there are about 93 in the U.S.), pass a state licensing exam (in some states), and perform experiential training under a licensed pharmacist. Once licensed, the pharmacist must receive continuing education to maintain their license.
cost control	A significant trend in recent health care has been the effort to control the cost of prescription drugs, on aspect of which is the use of closed "formularies" that rely substantially on substituting generic drugs in place of more expensive brands.
computerization	Pharmacy computer systems put customer profiles, product, inventory, pricing, and other essential information within easy access. One result has been that pharmacies and pharmacists dispense more prescriptions and information than ever before.

STUDY NOTES

Use this area to write important points you'd like to remember.

FILL IN THE KEY TERM

Use these key terms to fill in the correct blank. Answers are at the end of the book.

antibiotic	hormones	pharmaceutical
antitoxin	managed care	pharmacognosy
cocaine	OBRA-90	pharmacology
data	panacea	quinine
formularies	penicillin	salicylic acid

1. _____ :   A local anesthetic found in coca leaves.

2. _____ :   The natural drug derived from the bark of a white willow tree, used by the Ancient Greeks to relieve pain, and the natural forerunner to the active ingredient in aspirin.

3. _____ :   A drug for malaria found in cinchona bark.

4. _____ :   Of or about drugs; also, a drug product.

5. _____ :   A cure-all.

6. _____ :   The study of drugs—their properties, uses, application, and effects.

7. _____ :   A drug produced by a fungus that kills bacteria.

8. _____ :   The information stored in a computer.

9. _____ :   A substance that acts against a toxin in the body.

10. _____ :   A substance which harms or kills microorganisms like bacteria and fungi.

11. _____ :   Chemicals produced by the body that regulate body functions and processes.

12. _____ :   The study of physical, chemical, biochemical, and biological properties of drugs.

13. _____ :   U.S. legislation which required pharmacists to provide consulting services to Medicaid patients.

14. _____ :   Lists of drugs that are approved for use by patients.

15. _____ :   A major factor contributing to the attempt to control costs of prescription drugs.

TRUE/FALSE

Indicate whether the statement is true or false in the blank. Answers are at the end of the book.

_____ 1. The natural drug that is the forerunner to aspirin comes from the cinchona tree.

_____ 2. Most drugs used today are made synthetically.

_____ 3. Digitalis comes from the foxglove plant.

_____ 4. Cocaine was the first general anesthetic.

_____ 5. The average life span in the U.S. increased over 20 years in the twentieth century.

_____ 6. More pharmacists and technicians are employed in community pharmacies than in any other setting.

_____ 7. The second largest area of employment for pharmacists and technicians is home care.

_____ 8. The field of biotechnology has become the least dynamic area of pharmaceutical research and development.

_____ 9. According to Gallup Polls, pharmacists consistently rank as one of the most highly trusted and ethical professions in the United States.

_____ 10. Prescription drugs represent a large fraction of overall health care expenses.

EXPLAIN WHY

Explain why these statements are true or important. Check your answers in the text. Discuss any questions you may have with your Instructor.

1. Give at least three reasons why synthetic drugs are important.

2. Why was the use of anesthesia revolutionary?

3. Why was Paracelsus's work important?

4. Why was penicillin a major benefit in wartime?

5. Why is the Human Genome Project important to pharmacology?

6. Why are drug patents important?

7. Why are pharmacists among the most trusted professionals?

CHOOSE THE BEST ANSWER

Answers are at the end of the book.

1. The drug digitalis comes from the foxglove plant and is used to treat some _____ conditions.
   a. liver
   b. kidney
   c. heart
   d. lung

2. The first publicized operation using general anesthesia was performed using _____ as the anesthetic.
   a. cocaine
   b. foxglove
   c. quinine
   d. ether

3. The field of _____ has resulted from the study of the human genome.
   a. pharmacology
   b. biotechnology
   c. natural medicine
   d. discovery

4. Quinine comes from the bark of the cinchona and was used to treat
   a. malaria.
   b. diabetes.
   c. heart disease.
   d. hypertension.

5. The ancient Greek god of Medicine was
   a. Imhotep.
   b. Zeus.
   c. Aseculapius.
   d. Panacea.

6. _____ advocated "bleeding" to maintain balance of the "humours."
   a. Charaka
   b. Shen Nung
   c. Pontos
   d. Galen

7. _____ showed that an extract of insulin could lower blood sugar in dogs.
   a. Watson and Crick
   b. Banting and Best
   c. Fleming
   d. Hippocrates

8. An authoritative listing of drugs and issues related to their use is a (an)
   a. pharmacopeia.
   b. materia medica.
   c. panacea.
   d. Sumerian.

9. Care that is managed by an insurer is
   a. home care.
   b. managed care.
   c. short-term care.
   d. long-term care.

10. A substance that harms or kills microorganisms is called a(an)
    a. antitoxin.
    b. anesthetic.
    c. antibiotic.
    d. vaccine.

STUDY NOTES

Use this area to write important points you'd like to remember.

— 2 —

THE PHARMACY TECHNICIAN

KEY CONCEPTS

Test your knowledge by covering the information in the right hand column.

job responsibilities

Pharmacy technicians perform essential tasks that do not require the pharmacist's skill or expertise. Specific responsibilities and tasks differ by setting and are described in writing by each employer through job descriptions, policy and procedure manuals, and other documents.

supervision

Pharmacy technicians work under the direct supervision of a licensed pharmacist who is legally responsible for their performance.

pharmacist counseling

Having technicians assist the pharmacist frees the pharmacist for activities which require a greater level of expertise, such as counseling with patients.

scope of practice

What individuals may and may not do in their jobs is often referred to as their "scope of practice."

employment opportunities

Like pharmacists, most pharmacy technicians are employed in community pharmacies and hospitals. However, they are also employed in clinics, home care, long term care, mail order prescription pharmacies, and various other settings.

specialized jobs

In various hospital and other environments, there are specialized technician jobs which require more advanced skills developed from additional education, training, and experience.

trustworthiness

Pharmacy technicians are entrusted with confidential patient information, dangerous substances, and perishable products.

errors

Drugs, whether prescription or over the counter, can be dangerous if misused, and mistakes by pharmacy technicians can be life-threatening.

Health Insurance Portability and Accountability Act (HIPAA)	Pharmacy technicians are legally responsible for the privacy and security of protected health information (PHI).
math skills	Pharmacy technicians routinely perform mathematical calculations in filling prescriptions and other activities.
terminology	Pharmacy technicians must learn the specific pharmaceutical terminology that will be used on the job.
teamwork	Pharmacy technicians must be able to communicate, cooperate, and work effectively with others.
standards	There is no federal standard for pharmacy technician training or competency. However there are state and employer standards which must be met.
certification	A valuable career step for pharmacy technicians is getting certification by an appropriate organization or body. It verifies an individual's competence as a technician, and indicates a high level of knowledge and skill. In the United States, the Pharmacy Technician Certification Exam (PTCE) and the Exam for the Certification of Pharmacy Technicians (ExCPT) are national exams that lead to technician certification.

STUDY NOTES

Use this area to write important points you'd like to remember.

IN THE WORKPLACE

These sample job descriptions may help you in your career choice.

Sample Pharmacy Technician Job Description—Community Pharmacy

General Definition

The purpose of the pharmacy technician is to assist the pharmacist with the day-do-day activities in the pharmacy.

Responsibilities

- Help patients who are dropping off or picking up prescription orders
- Enter prescription orders into the computer
- Create a profile of the patient's health and insurance information in the computer or update the patient's profile
- Communicate with insurance carriers to obtain payment for prescription claims
- Complete weekly distribution center medication orders, place orders on shelves, and verify all associated paperwork
- Assist the pharmacist with filling and labeling prescriptions
- Prepare the pharmacy for inventory
- Screen telephone calls for the pharmacist
- Communicate with prescribers and their agents to obtain refill authorization
- Compound oral solutions, ointments, and creams
- Prepackage bulk medications

Qualifications

- Professional demeanor
- Ability to respect confidentiality of patient data
- Strong communication skills
- Courteous attitude
- Understanding of medical terminology and calculations
- Ability to type at least 35 words per minute
- Knowledge of computer operations
- Knowledge of medication brand and generic names
- Knowledge of insurance and third-party payment systems
- High school diploma or graduate equivalent degree
- National certification desirable

Sample Pharmacy Technician Job Description—Hospital Pharmacy

General Definition

Under the direction of a pharmacist, the pharmacy technician performs pharmacy-related functions, in compliance with department policies and procedures, that provide optimal pharmaceutical care.

Responsibilities

- Rotate through all work areas of the pharmacy
- Transport medications, drug-delivery devices, and other pharmacy equipment from the pharmacy to nursing units and clinics
- Pick up copies of physician orders, automated medication administration records, and unused medications from the nursing units and return them to the pharmacy
- Fill patient medication cassettes
- Prepare medications and supplies for dispensing, including:
  —prepackaging bulk medications
  —compounding ointments, creams, oral solutions, and other medications
  —preparing chemotherapeutic agents
  —compounding total parenteral nutrition solutions
  —compounding large-volume intravenous mixtures
  —packaging and preparing drugs being used in clinical investigations
  —preparing prescriptions for outpatients
- Assist pharmacists in entering medication orders into the computer system
- Prepare inventories, order drugs and supplies from the storeroom, receive drugs, and stock shelves in various pharmacy locations
- Screen telephone calls
- Perform monthly nursing unit inspections, maintain workload records, and collect quality-assurance data
- Assist in training new employees
- Assist other pharmacy technicians

Qualifications

- Valid state pharmacy technician registration (required in some states)
- High school diploma or graduate equivalent degree
- National certification desirable

Training and Experience

Must have one year of hospital pharmacy experience, have completed a pharmacy technician vocational course, or be a pharmacy student

Knowledge and Skills

- Ability to work as a team member
- Good communication skills
- Knowledge of basic pharmacy practices and procedures
- Knowledge of medications and medical supplies
- Strong mathematical computation skills
- Knowledge of record-keeping techniques
- Attention to detail
- Accurate typing skills (minimum 35 words per minute)
- Basic understanding of computer technology

IN THE WORKPLACE

This sample resume may help you when applying for a position as a pharmacy technician.

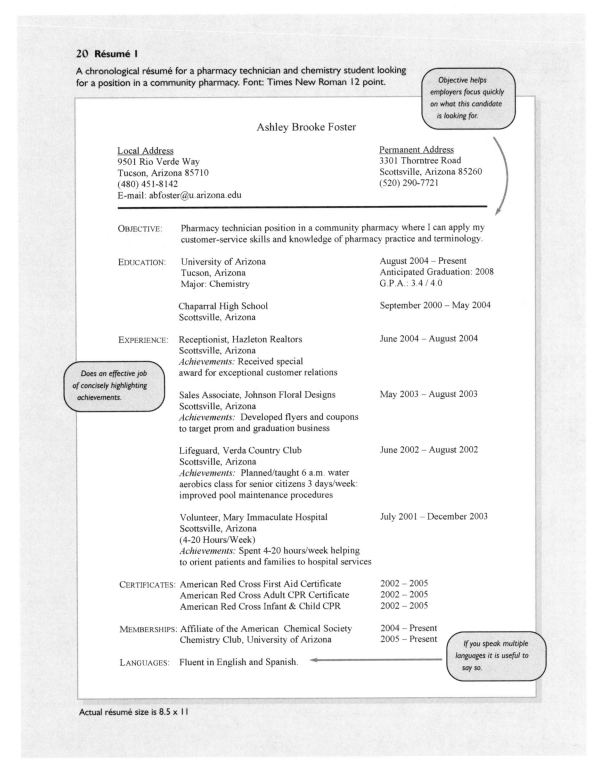

20 Resumé I

A chronological résumé for a pharmacy technician and chemistry student looking for a position in a community pharmacy. Font: Times New Roman 12 point.

Objective helps employers focus quickly on what this candidate is looking for.

Ashley Brooke Foster

Local Address
9501 Rio Verde Way
Tucson, Arizona 85710
(480) 451-8142
E-mail: abfoster@u.arizona.edu

Permanent Address
3301 Thorntree Road
Scottsville, Arizona 85260
(520) 290-7721

OBJECTIVE: Pharmacy technician position in a community pharmacy where I can apply my customer-service skills and knowledge of pharmacy practice and terminology.

EDUCATION: University of Arizona   August 2004 – Present
Tucson, Arizona   Anticipated Graduation: 2008
Major: Chemistry   G.P.A.: 3.4 / 4.0

Chaparral High School   September 2000 – May 2004
Scottsville, Arizona

EXPERIENCE: Receptionist, Hazleton Realtors   June 2004 – August 2004
Scottsville, Arizona
Achievements: Received special
award for exceptional customer relations

Does an effective job of concisely highlighting achievements.

Sales Associate, Johnson Floral Designs   May 2003 – August 2003
Scottsville, Arizona
Achievements: Developed flyers and coupons
to target prom and graduation business

Lifeguard, Verda Country Club   June 2002 – August 2002
Scottsville, Arizona
Achievements: Planned/taught 6 a.m. water
aerobics class for senior citizens 3 days/week:
improved pool maintenance procedures

Volunteer, Mary Immaculate Hospital   July 2001 – December 2003
Scottsville, Arizona
(4-20 Hours/Week)
Achievements: Spent 4-20 hours/week helping
to orient patients and families to hospital services

CERTIFICATES: American Red Cross First Aid Certificate   2002 – 2005
American Red Cross Adult CPR Certificate   2002 – 2005
American Red Cross Infant & Child CPR   2002 – 2005

MEMBERSHIPS: Affiliate of the American Chemical Society   2004 – Present
Chemistry Club, University of Arizona   2005 – Present

If you speak multiple languages it is useful to say so.

LANGUAGES: Fluent in English and Spanish.

Actual résumé size is 8.5 x 11

Source: Reproduced by permission from *The Pharmacy Professional's Guide to Résumés, CV's & Interviewing* (Washington, D.C. American Pharmacists Association, 2006), pp. 20-23. © Copyright 2006 by the American Pharmacists Association.

IN THE WORKPLACE

These sample resumes may help you when applying for a position as a pharmacy technician.

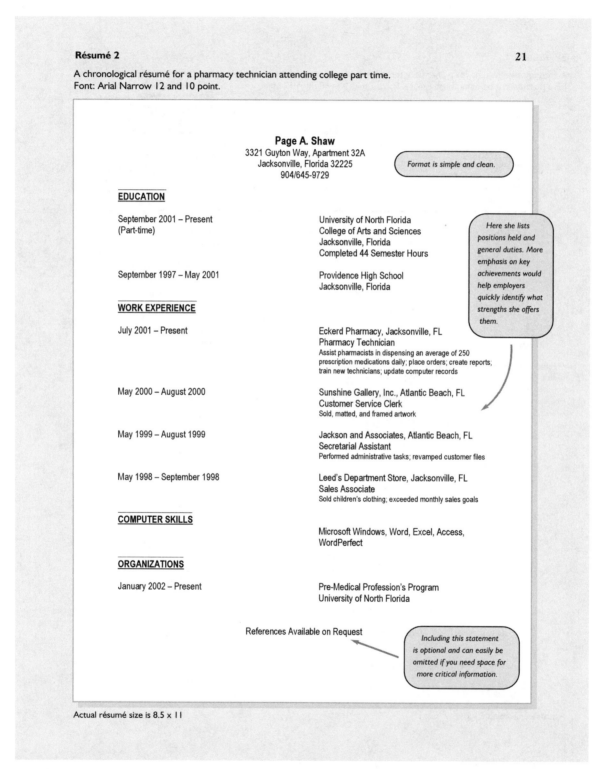

Résumé 2   21

A chronological résumé for a pharmacy technician attending college part time.
Font: Arial Narrow 12 and 10 point.

Page A. Shaw
3321 Guyton Way, Apartment 32A
Jacksonville, Florida 32225
904/645-9729

Format is simple and clean.

EDUCATION

September 2001 – Present
(Part-time)

University of North Florida
College of Arts and Sciences
Jacksonville, Florida
Completed 44 Semester Hours

Here she lists positions held and general duties. More emphasis on key achievements would help employers quickly identify what strengths she offers them.

September 1997 – May 2001

Providence High School
Jacksonville, Florida

WORK EXPERIENCE

July 2001 – Present

Eckerd Pharmacy, Jacksonville, FL
Pharmacy Technician
Assist pharmacists in dispensing an average of 250
prescription medications daily; place orders; create reports;
train new technicians; update computer records

May 2000 – August 2000

Sunshine Gallery, Inc., Atlantic Beach, FL
Customer Service Clerk
Sold, matted, and framed artwork

May 1999 – August 1999

Jackson and Associates, Atlantic Beach, FL
Secretarial Assistant
Performed administrative tasks; revamped customer files

May 1998 – September 1998

Leed's Department Store, Jacksonville, FL
Sales Associate
Sold children's clothing; exceeded monthly sales goals

COMPUTER SKILLS

Microsoft Windows, Word, Excel, Access,
WordPerfect

ORGANIZATIONS

January 2002 – Present

Pre-Medical Profession's Program
University of North Florida

References Available on Request

Including this statement is optional and can easily be omitted if you need space for more critical information.

Actual résumé size is 8.5 x 11

Source: Reproduced by permission from *The Pharmacy Professional's Guide to Résumés, CV's & Interviewing* (Washington, D.C. American Pharmacists Association, 2006), pp. 20-23. © Copyright 2006 by the American Pharmacists Association.

22 Résumé 3

Chronological résumé of a certified pharmacy technician enrolled in a pre-pharmacy course of study.
Font: Arial 12 point.

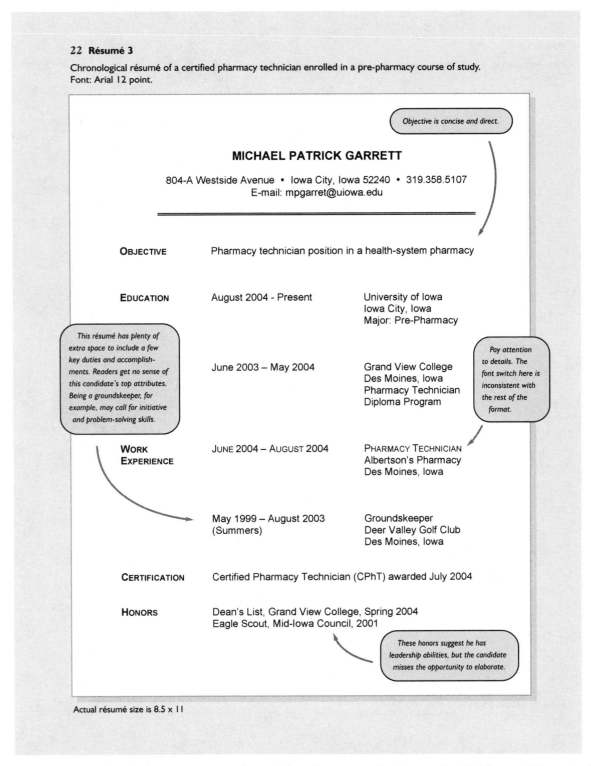

Objective is concise and direct.

MICHAEL PATRICK GARRETT

804-A Westside Avenue • Iowa City, Iowa 52240 • 319.358.5107
E-mail: mpgarret@uiowa.edu

OBJECTIVE	Pharmacy technician position in a health-system pharmacy	
EDUCATION	August 2004 - Present	University of Iowa Iowa City, Iowa Major: Pre-Pharmacy
	June 2003 – May 2004	Grand View College Des Moines, Iowa Pharmacy Technician Diploma Program
WORK EXPERIENCE	JUNE 2004 – AUGUST 2004	PHARMACY TECHNICIAN Albertson's Pharmacy Des Moines, Iowa
	May 1999 – August 2003 (Summers)	Groundskeeper Deer Valley Golf Club Des Moines, Iowa
CERTIFICATION	Certified Pharmacy Technician (CPhT) awarded July 2004	
HONORS	Dean's List, Grand View College, Spring 2004 Eagle Scout, Mid-Iowa Council, 2001	

This résumé has plenty of extra space to include a few key duties and accomplishments. Readers get no sense of this candidate's top attributes. Being a groundskeeper, for example, may call for initiative and problem-solving skills.

Pay attention to details. The font switch here is inconsistent with the rest of the format.

These honors suggest he has leadership abilities, but the candidate misses the opportunity to elaborate.

Actual résumé size is 8.5 x 11

Source: Reproduced by permission from *The Pharmacy Professional's Guide to Résumés, CV's & Interviewing* (Washington, D.C. American Pharmacists Association, 2006), pp. 20-23. © Copyright 2006 by the American Pharmacists Association.

IN THE WORKPLACE

This sample resume may help you when applying for admission to pharmacy school.

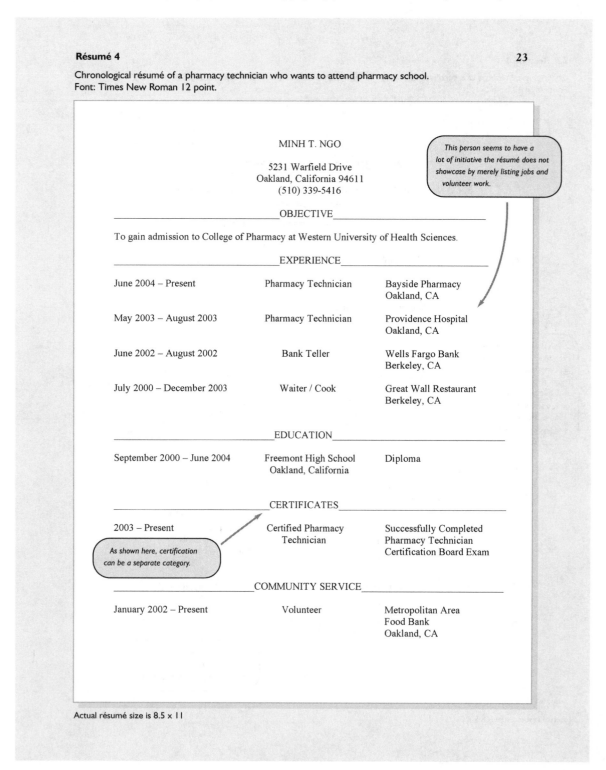

Résumé 4   23

Chronological résumé of a pharmacy technician who wants to attend pharmacy school.
Font: Times New Roman 12 point.

MINH T. NGO

5231 Warfield Drive
Oakland, California 94611
(510) 339-5416

This person seems to have a lot of initiative the résumé does not showcase by merely listing jobs and volunteer work.

_____OBJECTIVE_____

To gain admission to College of Pharmacy at Western University of Health Sciences.

_____EXPERIENCE_____

June 2004 – Present	Pharmacy Technician	Bayside Pharmacy Oakland, CA
May 2003 – August 2003	Pharmacy Technician	Providence Hospital Oakland, CA
June 2002 – August 2002	Bank Teller	Wells Fargo Bank Berkeley, CA
July 2000 – December 2003	Waiter / Cook	Great Wall Restaurant Berkeley, CA

_____EDUCATION_____

| September 2000 – June 2004 | Freemont High School Oakland, California | Diploma |

_____CERTIFICATES_____

| 2003 – Present | Certified Pharmacy Technician | Successfully Completed Pharmacy Technician Certification Board Exam |

As shown here, certification can be a separate category.

_____COMMUNITY SERVICE_____

| January 2002 – Present | Volunteer | Metropolitan Area Food Bank Oakland, CA |

Actual résumé size is 8.5 x 11

Source: Reproduced by permission from *The Pharmacy Professional's Guide to Résumés, CV's & Interviewing* (Washington, D.C. American Pharmacists Association, 2006), pp. 20-23. © Copyright 2006 by the American Pharmacists Association.

FILL IN THE KEY TERM

Use these key terms to fill in the correct blank. Answers are at the end of the book.

ASHP	detail oriented	probation period
certification	patient welfare	professionals
competent	performance review	scope of practice
confidentiality	personal inventory	technicians
continuing education	pharmacist	

1. _____ : What individuals may and may not do in their jobs.

2. _____ : To assess characteristics, skills, qualities, etc.

3. _____ : The requirement of health care providers to keep all patient information private among the patient, the patient's insurer, and the providers directly involved in the patient's care.

4. _____ : The most important consideration in health care.

5. _____ : Being qualified and capable to perform a task or job.

6. _____ : A legal proof or document that an individual meets certain objective standards, usually provided by a neutral professional organization.

7. _____ : Individuals who are given a basic level of training designed to help them perform specific tasks.

8. _____ : Individuals who receive extensive and advanced levels of education before being allowed to practice, such as physicians and pharmacists.

9. _____ : Technicians always work under their direct supervision.

10. _____ : Employer documents employee's job competency.

11. _____ : Has model curriculum for technician training.

12. _____ : A highly important personal characteristic for technicians, since mistakes with drugs can be life-threatening.

13. _____ : A critical element in maintaining competency for pharmacy technicians.

14. _____ : Period of time for a new employee to learn the skill set for a job.

TRUE/FALSE

Indicate whether the statement is true or false in the blank. Answers are at the end of the book.

_____ 1.   Specific technician responsibilities differ by setting and job description.

_____ 2.   Technicians may sometimes provide counseling services to patients.

_____ 3.   Most pharmacy technicians are employed in hospitals.

_____ 4.   Mathematics skills are very important to the pharmacy technician.

_____ 5.   It is essential for technicians to have good interpersonal skills.

_____ 6.   The U.S. government sets standards for technician training.

_____ 7.   PHI is considered public information.

_____ 8.   Employers monitor the performance and competency of technicians on an ongoing basis.

_____ 9.   The ASHP has developed a national model curriculum for pharmacy technicians.

_____ 10. Once earned, the CPhT designation applies for life and does not require renewal.

EXPLAIN WHY

Explain why these statements are true or important. Check your answers in the text. Discuss any questions you may have with your Instructor.

1. Give at least two reasons technicians must work under the supervision of a pharmacist.

2. Why is knowing your "scope of practice important?"

3. Why is dependability important?

4. Why is it important that pharmacy technicians understand their responsibilities under the 1996 Health Insurance Portability and Accountability Act (HIPAA)?

5. Why should technicians have math skills?

6. Why are interpersonal skills important?

7. Why is certification a good idea for technicians?

8. Why is continuing education valuable for technicians?

CHOOSE THE BEST ANSWER

Answers are at the end of the book.

1. When technicians perform appropriate essential tasks, this allows the pharmacist time for tasks requiring more advanced professional expertise such as
   a. telephoning insurance companies.
   b. consulting with patients.
   c. counting tablets.
   d. ringing the cash register.

2. Taking routine patient information is a duty of the
   a. consultant.
   b. cashier.
   c. pharmacist.
   d. pharmacy technician.

3. Pharmacy technicians should be dependable. This means
   a. technicians' work can always be done by pharmacists.
   b. technicians are not as important as pharmacists.
   c. the patient, the pharmacist, and the patient's health care team will depend on the technician to perform his/her job as required, whether or not anyone is observing.
   d. tardiness is acceptable.

4. Do pharmacy technicians need to maintain good physical and mental health?
   a. Yes, to decrease the chance of making serious mistakes.
   b. Yes, because some belong to labor unions.
   c. No. Pharmacists are always responsible for the technician, so technicians don't have to worry about getting enough sleep.
   d. No. Pharmacists have more education and so will catch all errors made.

5. According to HIPAA, it is ok to
   a. discuss patient information within earshot of other patients.
   b. bill insurance using HIPAA-compliant EDI.
   c. bill insurance using non-secure EDI.
   d. casually discuss a patient's condition with a patient's spouse.

6. _____ accredits pharmacy technician training programs.
   a. PTCB
   b. APhA
   c. PTEC
   d. ASHP

7. _____ are regularly scheduled events to monitor and document technician competency.
   a. PTCE
   b. PTCB
   c. Performance reviews
   d. JCAHO

8. _____ is a legal proof or document that an individual meets certain objective standards, usually provided by a neutral professional organization.
   a. Registration
   b. Certification
   c. Documentation
   d. Prior authorization

9. CPhT stands for
   a. Certified Pharmacy Trainer.
   b. Complete Pharmacy Technician.
   c. Certified Pharmacy Technician.
   d. Certified Pharmacist Technician.

10. To pass the PTCE, candidates must score at least
   a. 550.
   b. 600.
   c. 650.
   d. 750.

— 3 —

DRUG REGULATION & CONTROL

KEY CONCEPTS

Test your knowledge by covering the information in the right hand column.

Food and Drug Administration	The leading enforcement agency at the federal level for regulations concerning drug products.
Drug Enforcement Administration	The agency which controls the distribution of drugs that may be easily abused.
Food and Drug Act of 1906	Prohibited interstate commerce in adulterated or misbranded food, drinks, and drugs. Government pre-approval of drugs is required.
1938 Food, Drug and Cosmetic (FDC) Act	In response to the fatal poisoning of 107 people, primarily children, by an untested sulfanilamide concoction, this comprehensive law requires new drugs be shown to be safe before marketing.
1951 Durham-Humphrey Amendment	This law defines what drugs require a prescription by a licensed practitioner and requires them to include this legend on the label: "Caution: Federal Law prohibits dispensing without a prescription."
1962 Kefauver-Harris Amendments	Requires drug manufacturers to provide proof of both safety and effectiveness before marketing the drug.
1970 Poison Prevention Packaging Act	Requires child-proof packaging on all controlled and most prescription drugs dispensed by pharmacies.
1970 Controlled Substances Act (CSA)	The CSA classifies drugs that may be easily abused and restricts their distribution. It is enforced by the Drug Enforcement Administration (DEA) within the Justice Department.
1990 Omnibus Budget Reconciliation Act (OBRA)	Among other things, this act required pharmacists to offer counseling to Medicaid patients regarding medications, effectively putting the common practice into law.

1996 Health Insurance Portability and Accountability Act (HIPAA)	Provided broad and stringent regulations to protect patients' privacy.
placebos	Inactive substances, not real medications, that are used to test the effectiveness of drugs.
new drugs	All new drugs, whether made domestically or imported, require FDA approval before they can be marketed in the United States.
clinical tests	Tests on proposed new drugs (investigational drugs) are "controlled" by comparing the effect of a proposed drug on one group of patients with the effect of a different treatment on other patients.
blind tests	Patients in a trial are always "blind" to the treatment, i.e., they are not told which control group they are in. In a "double-blind" test, neither the patients nor the physicians know what the medication is.
patent protection	A patent for a new drug gives its manufacturer an exclusive right to market the drug for a specific period of time under a brand name. A drug patent is in effect for 17 years from the date of the drug's discovery. The Hatch-Waxman Act of 1984 provided for up to five year extensions of patent protection to the patent holders to make up for time lost while products went through the FDA approval process.
generics	Once a patent for a brand drug expires, other manufacturers may copy the drug and release it under its pharmaceutical or "generic" name.
labels and product labeling	All drugs are required to have clear and accurate information for all labels, inserts, packaging, and so on, but there are different information requirements for various categories of drugs.
prescription drug labels	The minimum requirements on prescription labels for most drugs are as follows: name and address of dispenser, prescription serial number, date of prescription or filling, name of prescriber, name of patient, directions for use, and cautionary statements.
NDC (National Drug Code) number	The number assigned by the manufacturer. Each NDC number has three parts or sets of numbers: The first set indicates the manufacturer; the next set indicates the medication, its strength, and dosage form; the last set indicates the package size.

KEY CONCEPTS

Test your knowledge by covering the information in the right hand column.

controlled substances

A drug which has the potential to be abused and for which distribution is controlled by one of five "schedules."

control classifications

Manufacturers must clearly label controlled drugs with their control classification.

DEA number/formula

The **number** all prescribers of controlled substances are assigned and which must be used on all controlled drug prescriptions. It has two letters followed by seven single-digit numbers, e.g., AB1234563. The **formula** for checking a DEA number on a prescription form is: if the sum of the first, third and fifth digits is added to twice the sum of the second, fourth, and sixth digits, the total should be a number whose last digit is the same as the last digit of the DEA number.

risks of approved drugs

There is always the risk that an approved drug may produce adverse side effects when used on a larger population.

recalls

Recalls are, with a few exceptions, voluntary on the part of the manufacturer. There are three classes of recalls: I. where there is a strong likelihood that the product will cause serious adverse effects or death; II. where a product may cause temporary but reversible adverse effects, or in which there is little likelihood of serious adverse effects; III. where a product is not likely to cause adverse effects.

MedWatch

FDA reporting program for health care professionals to report adverse effects that occur from the use of an approved drug or other medical product. The MedWatch Online Voluntary Reporting Form 3500 is used for FDA-regulated drugs, biologics, medical devices, and special nutritional products and cosmetics.

state regulations

State boards of pharmacy are responsible for licensing all prescribers and dispensers and administering regulations for the practice of pharmacy in the state.

liability

Legal liability means you can be prosecuted for misconduct.

negligence

Failing to do something that should or must be done.

CONTROLLED SUBSTANCE SCHEDULES

The five control schedules are as follows*:

Schedule I:

➥ Each drug has a high potential for abuse and no accepted medical use in the United States. It may not be prescribed. Heroin, various opium derivatives, and hallucinogenic substances are included on this schedule.

Schedule II:

➥ Each drug has a high potential for abuse and may lead to physical or psychological dependence, but also has a currently accepted medical use in the United States. Amphetamines, opium, cocaine, methadone, and various opiates are included on this schedule.

Schedule III:

➥ Each drug's potential for abuse is less than those in Schedules I and II and there is a currently accepted medical use in the U.S., but abuse may lead to moderate or low physical dependence or high psychological dependence. Anabolic steroids and various compounds containing limited quantities of narcotic substances such as codeine are included on this schedule.

Schedule IV:

➥ Each drug has a low potential for abuse relative to Schedule III drugs and there is a current accepted medical use in the U.S., but abuse may lead to limited physical dependence or psychological dependence. Phenobarbital, the sedative chloral hydrate, and the anesthetic methohexital are included in this group.

Schedule V:

➥ Each drug has a low potential for abuse relative to Schedule IV drugs and there is a current accepted medical use in the U.S., but abuse may lead to limited physical dependence or psychological dependence. Compounds containing limited amounts of a narcotic such as codeine are included in this group.

*21 USC Sec. 812. Source: http://www.deadiversion.usdoj.gov/21cfr/21usc/812.htm. Note: These schedules are revised periodically. It is important to refer to the most current schedule.

Controlled-Substance Prescriptions

Controlled-substance prescriptions have greater requirements at both federal and state levels than other prescriptions, particularly Schedule II drugs. On controlled substance prescriptions, the DEA number must appear on the form and the patient's full street address must be entered.

On Schedule II prescriptions, the form must be signed by the prescriber. In many states, there are specific time limits that require Schedule II prescriptions be promptly filled. Generally, quantities are limited and no refills are allowed.

Federal requirements for Schedules III–V are less stringent than for Schedule II. *For example, Schedules III–V prescriptions may be refilled up to five times within six months.* However, state and other regulations may be stricter than federal requirements, so it is necessary to know the requirements for your specific job setting.

APPROVED DRUG PRODUCTS WITH THERAPEUTIC EQUIVALENCE EVALUATIONS (THE "ORANGE BOOK")

The FDA annually publishes *Approved Drug Products With Therapeutic Equivalence Evaluations* (the "Orange Book"). The "Orange Book" provides a two letter evaluation code to allow users to determine whether the FDA has evaluated a particular product as therapeutically equivalent to other pharmaceutically equivalent products (first letter) and to provide additional information on the basis of FDA's evaluations (second letter).

"**A**" drug products are those the FDA considers to be therapeutically equivalent to other pharmaceutically equivalent products. There are (1) no known or suspected bioequivalence problems or (2) the actual or potential bioequivalence problems have been resolved with adequate in vivo and/or in vitro evidence supporting bioequivalence.

"**B**" drug products are those the FDA considers not to be therapeutically equivalent to other pharmaceutically equivalent products. Often, the problem is with specific dosage forms rather than with the active ingredient.

A listing of the codes is below:

AA	Products in conventional dosage forms not presenting bioequivalence problems
AB	Products meeting bioequivalence requirements
AN	Solutions and powders for aerosolization
AO	Injectable oil solutions
AP	Injectable aqueous solutions
AT	Topical products
BC	Extended-release tablets, extended-release capsules, and extended-release injectables
BD	Active ingredients and dosage forms with documented bioequivalence problems
BE	Delayed-release oral dosage forms
BN	Products in aerosol-nebulizer drug delivery systems
BP	Active ingredients and dosage forms with potential bioequivalence problems
BR	Suppositories or enemas for systemic use
BS	Products with drug standard deficiencies
BT	Topical products with bioequivalence issues
BX	Insufficient data

There are some products that cannot be described with just the two letter code, i.e., a more complete explanation is needed. These products often have problems with identity, analytical methodology, or bioequivalence standards. For some of these products, bioequivalence has not been established or no generic product is currently available.

The "Orange Book" can be found on the web at http://www.fda.gov/cder/ob/default.htm.

FILL IN THE KEY TERM

Use these key terms to fill in the correct blank. Answers are at the end of the book.

adverse effect   legend drug   pediatric
controlled substance mark   liability   placebo
DEA number   "look-alike" regulation   product labeling
exempt narcotics   NDC (National Drug Code)   recall
injunction   negligence   therapeutic

1. _____ : The number all prescribers of controlled substances are assigned and which must be used on all controlled drug prescriptions.

2. _____ : A court order preventing a specific action, such as the distribution of a potentially dangerous drug.

3. _____ : An inactive substance given in place of a medication.

4. _____ : An unintended side affect of a medication that is negative or in some way injurious to a patient's health.

5. _____ : Any drug which requires a prescription and this "legend" on the label: Rx only.

6. _____ : Failing to do something you should have done.

7. _____ : Having to do with the treatment of children.

8. _____ : Important associated information that is not on the label of a drug product itself.

9. _____ : Federal laws require that a drug and/or its container not be imitative of another drug so that the consumer will be misled.

10. _____ : Means you can be prosecuted for misconduct.

11. _____ : The action taken to remove a drug from the market and have it returned to the manufacturer.

12. _____ : The mark (CII-CV) which indicates the control category of a drug with a potential for abuse.

13. _____ : The number on a manufacturer's label indicating the manufacturer and product information.

14. _____ : Medications with habit-forming ingredients that could be dispensed by a pharmacist without a prescription.

True/False

Indicate whether the statement is true or false in the blank. Answers are at the end of the book.

_____ 1. Child-proof packaging was required by the Fair Packaging and Labeling Act.

_____ 2. The CMEA sets daily and monthly restrictions on the sale of pseudoephedrine.

_____ 3. Only about 25% of drugs tested on humans are approved for use by the FDA.

_____ 4. Over-the-counter medications do not require a prescription but sometimes prescriptions are written for them.

_____ 5. A prescription serial number must appear on the label of a dispensed prescription container.

_____ 6. A Class III recall is most likely to cause harm or death.

_____ 7. Negligence is the most common form of misconduct.

_____ 8. Schedule III, IV, and V drugs may be stored openly on shelves in retail and hospital settings.

_____ 9. All controlled substances must be ordered using a DEA controlled substance order form.

_____ 10. Most recalls are voluntary.

Explain Why

Explain why these statements are true or important. Check your answers in the text. Discuss any questions you may have with your Instructor.

1. Why is blind testing used in the drug approval process?

2. Give three reasons why OTC labels should be clear and understandable.

3. Why are some drugs "controlled" by the DEA?

4. Why are some drug patents extended past the original 17 year period?

5. Why would a manufacturer want to recall a drug product?

6. Give three reasons why failing to do something could result in a criminal charge of negligence.

MATCH THE TERM — CONTROLLED SUBSTANCES AND RECALLS

Use these key terms to fill in the correct blank. Answers are at the end of the book.

Schedule I Drugs   **Schedule V Drugs**
Schedule II Drugs   **Class I Recall**
Schedule III Drugs   **Class II Recall**
Schedule IV Drugs   **Class III Recall**

1. _____ :   Amphetamines, opium, cocaine, methadone, and various opiates are included on this schedule.

2. _____ :   Anabolic steroids and various compounds containing limited quantities of narcotic substances such as codeine are included on this schedule.

3. _____ :   When a product is not likely to cause adverse effects.

4. _____ :   Compounds containing limited amounts of a narcotic such as codeine are included in this group.

5. _____ :   When a product may cause temporary but reversible adverse effects, or in which there is little likelihood of serious adverse effects.

6. _____ :   Heroin, various opium derivatives, and hallucinogenic substances are included on this schedule.

7. _____ :   Phenobarbital, the sedative chloral hydrate, and the anesthetic methohexital are included in this group.

8. _____ :   When there is a strong likelihood that the product will cause serious adverse effects or death.

IDENTIFY

Identify the required elements on this manufacturer's bottle label by answering in the space beneath the question.

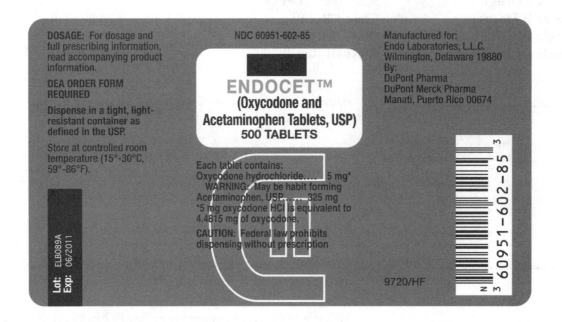

1. In what kind of container should this medication be dispensed?

2. Who is the manufacturer of this drug product?

3. What is the product's brand name?

4. What is the product's generic name?

5. What is the drug form?

6. What are the active ingredients?

7. What control level is the drug product?

8. What are the storage requirements?

9. What is the expiration date?

CHOOSE THE BEST ANSWER

Answers are at the end of the book.

1. The _____ defined what drugs require a prescription.
   a. 1970 Poison Prevention Packaging Act
   b. 1962 Kefauver-Harris Amendment
   c. Sherley Amendment
   d. 1951 Durham-Humphrey Amendment

2. A need for tighter drug regulations from the thalidomide lesson led to the
   a. Kefauver-Harris Amendment.
   b. Durham-Humphrey Amendment.
   c. Food and Drug Act of 1906.
   d. Food Drug and Cosmetic Act.

3. Legend drugs should have the legend _____ on the manufacturer's label.
   a. "Federal law prohibits transfer of this prescription"
   b. "Store at room temperature"
   c. "For external use only"
   d. "RX only"

4. In clinical trials, the testing is done
   a. on mice.
   b. on people.
   c. in vitro.
   d. on dogs.

5. The main purpose of phase I clinical trials is
   a. efficacy.
   b. dosage.
   c. safety.
   d. economics.

6. The daily sales limit of pseudoephedrine base is
   a. 3.6 g per household.
   b. 3.6 g per purchaser.
   c. 3.6 g per transaction.

7. The national drug code (NDC) is assigned by the
   a. FDA.
   b. DEA.
   c. CDER.
   d. manufacturer.

8. DEA form _____ is used to order Schedule II controlled substances.
   a. 41
   b. 106
   c. 222
   d. 224

9. In each state, pharmacists are licensed by the
   a. DEA.
   b. FDA.
   c. federal government.
   d. state board of pharmacy.

10. Doing what is required is
    a. compliance.
    b. a protocol.
    c. liability.
    d. exempt.

— 4 —

TERMINOLOGY

KEY CONCEPTS

Test your knowledge by covering the information in the right hand column.

terminology	Much of medical science is made up of a small number of root words, suffixes, and prefixes that originated from either Greek or Latin words.
root word	The base component of a term which gives it a meaning that may be modified by other components.
prefix	A modifying component of a term located before the other components of the term.
suffix	A modifying component of a term located after the other components of the term.
combining vowel	Combining vowels are used to connect the prefix, root, or suffix parts of the term.
cardiovascular system	Distributes blood throughout the body using blood vessels called arteries, capillaries, and veins.
endocrine system	Consists of the glands that secrete hormones (chemicals that assist in regulating body functions).
gastrointestinal (GI) tract	Contains the organs that are involved in the digestion of foods and the absorption of nutrients.
integumentary system	The body's first line of defense, acting as a barrier against disease and other hazards.
lymphatic system	The center of the body's immune system. Lymphocytes are a white blood cell that helps the body defend itself against bacteria and diseased cells.
muscular system	The body contains more than 600 muscles which give shape and movement to it.

nervous system	The body's system of communication. The neuron (nerve cell) is its basic functional unit.
skeletal system	Protects soft organs and provides structure and support for the body's organ systems.
female reproductive system	Produces hormones (estrogen, progesterone), controls menstruation, and provides for childbearing.
male reproductive system	Produces sperm and secretes the hormone testosterone.
respiratory system	Brings oxygen into the body through inhalation and expels carbon dioxide gas through exhalation.
urinary tract	The primary organ is the kidney, which filters the blood for unwanted material and makes urine.
ear	The sense of hearing, as well as the maintenance of body equilibrium, is performed by the ear.
eyes	The eyelids protect the eye and assist in its lubrication. The conjunctiva is the blood-rich membrane between the eye and the eyelid.
drug classifications	A grouping of a number of drugs that have some properties in common. The same steps in interpreting other medical science terminology can be used to interpret drug classification names.

STUDY NOTES

Use this area to write important points you'd like to remember.

ORGAN SYSTEM ROOTS

CARDIOVASCULAR SYSTEM

angi	vessel
aort	aorta
card	heart
oxy	oxygen
pector	chest
phleb	vein
stenosis	narrowing
thromb	clot
vas(cu)	blood vessel
ven	vein

ENDOCRINE SYSTEM

adrena	adrenal
glyc	sugar
lipid	fat
nephr	kidney
pancreat	pancreas
somat	body
thym	thymus

GASTROINTESTINAL SYSTEM

chol	bile
col	colon
duoden	duodenum
enter	intestine
esophag	esophagus
gastr	stomach
hepat	liver
lapar	abdomen
pancreat	pancreas

INTEGUMENTARY SYSTEM

adip	fat
cutane	skin
derma	skin
hist	tissue
kerat	hard
mast	breast
necr	death (cells, body)
onych	nail

LYMPHATIC SYSTEM

aden	gland
cyt	cell
hemo, hemat	blood
lymph	lymph
splen	spleen
thromb	clot
thym	thymus

MUSCULAR SYSTEM

chondr	cartilage
my	muscle
fibr	fiber
tendin	tendon

NERVOUS SYSTEM

cerebr	cerebrum
dementio	to be mad
encephal	brain
esthesi	sensation
mening	meninges
myel	spinal cord
neur	nerve

SKELETAL SYSTEM

arthr	joint
carp	wrist
crani	cranium
dactyl	finger or toe
femor	thigh bone
fibul	small, outer lower leg bone
humer	humerus
oste	bone
patell	kneecap
ped, pod	foot
pelv	pelvis
phalang	bones of fingers and toes
rachi	spinal cord, vertebrae
spondy	backbone, vertebrae
stern	sternum, breastbone
tibi	large lower leg bone

ORGAN SYSTEM ROOTS

FEMALE REPRODUCTIVE SYSTEM

gynec	woman
hyster	uterus
lact	milk
mamm	breast
mast	breast
metr	uterus
ovari	ovary
salping	fallopian tube
toc	birth
uter	uterine

MALE REPRODUCTIVE SYSTEM

andr	male
balan	glans penis
orchid, test	testis, testicle
prostat	prostate gland
sperm	sperm
vas	vessel, duct
vesicul	seminal vescles

RESPIRATORY SYSTEM

aer	air
aero	gas
bronch	bronchus
capn	carbon dioxide
laryng	larynx
nasal	nose
ox	oxygen
pector	chest
pneum	lung, air
pulmon	lung
sinus	sinus

URINARY TRACT

albumin	protein
cyst	bladder
nephr	kidney
ren	kidney
ureter	ureter
urethr	urethra
uria	urine, urination
vesic	bladder

HEARING

acous	hearing
acusis	hearing condition
audi	hearing
cerumin	wax-like, waxy
myring	eardrum
ot	ear
salping	eustachian tube
tympan	eardrum

SIGHT

blephar	eyelid
cor	pupil
dacry, lacrim	tear, tear duct
irid, iri	iris
ocul	eye
ophthalm	eye
retin	retina

STUDY NOTES

Use this area to write important points you'd like to remember.

COMMON PREFIXES

a	without		melan	black
ambi	both		meso	middle
an	without		meta	beyond, after, changing
ante	before		micro	small
anti	against		mid	middle
bi	two or both		mono	one
brady	slow		multi	many
chlor	green		neo	new
circum	around		pan	all
cirrh	yellow		para	alongside or abnormal
con	with		peri	around
contra	against		polio	gray
cyan	blue		poly	many
dia	across or through		post	after
dis	separate from or apart		pre	before
dys	painful, difficult		pro	before
ec	away or out		pseudo	false
ecto	outside		purpur	purple
endo	within		quadri	four
epi	upon		re	again or back
erythr	red		retro	after
eu	good or normal		rube	red
exo	outside		semi	half
hemi	half		sub	below or under
hyper	above or excessive		super	above or excessive
hypo	below or deficient		supra	above or excessive
im	not		sym	with
immun	safe, protected		syn	with
in	not		tachy	fast
infra	below or under		trans	across, through
inter	between		tri	three
intra	within		ultra	beyond or excessive
iso	equal		uni	one
leuk	white		xanth	yellow
macro	large		xer	dry
medi	middle			

COMMON SUFFIXES

ac	pertaining to		ole	small
al	pertaining to		oma	tumor
algia	pain		opia	vision
ar	pertaining to		opsia	vision
ary	pertaining to		osis	abnormal condition
asthenia	without strength		osmia	smell
cele	pouching or hernia		ous	pertaining to
cyesis	pregnancy		paresis	partial paralysis
cynia	pain		pathy	disease
eal	pertaining to		penia	decrease
ectasis	expansion or dilation		phagia	swallowing
ectomy	removal		phasia	speech
emia	blood condition		philia	attraction for
genic	origin or production		phobia	fear
gram	record		plasia	formation
graph	recording instrument		plasty	surgical reconstruction
graphy	recording process		plegia	paralysis, stroke
ia	condition of		rrhage	to burst forth
iasis	condition, formation of		rrhea	discharge
iatry	treatment		sclerosis	narrowing, constriction
ic	pertaining to		scope	examination instrument
icle	small		scopy	examination
ism	condition of		spasm	involuntary contraction
itis	inflammation		stasis	stop or stand
ium	tissue		tic	pertaining to
lith	stone, calculus		tocia	childbirth, labor
logy	study of		tomy	incision
malacia	softening		toxic	poison
megaly	enlargement		tropic	stimulate
meter	measuring instrument		ula	small
metry	measuring process		ule	small
mycosis	fungal infection		y	condition, process of
oi	resembling			

COMMON MEDICAL ABBREVIATIONS

ABG	Arterial blood gases		IOP	Intraocular pressure
ADD	Attention deficit disorder		IV	Intravenous
AIDS	Acquired immunodeficiency syndrome		KVO	Keep vein open
AV	Atrial-ventricular		LBW	Low birth weight
AMI	Acute myocardial infarction		LDL	Low density lipoprotein
ANS	Autonomic nervous system		LOC	Loss of consciousness
BM	Bowel movement		MI	Myocardial infarction
BP	Blood pressure		MICU	Medical intensive care unit
BPH	Benign prostatic hyperplasia		MRI	Magnetic resonance imaging
BS	Blood sugar		NKA	No known allergies
BSA	Body surface area		NPO	Nothing by mouth
CA	Cancer		NVD	Nausea, vomiting, diarrhea
CABG	Coronary artery bypass graft		OR	Operating room
CAD	Coronary artery disease		PAP	Pulmonary artery pressure
CF	Cardiac failure		PMH	Past medical history
CHF	Congestive heart failure		PUD	Peptic ulcer disease
CMV	Cytomegalovirus		PVD	Peripheral vascular disease
CNS	Central nervous system		RA	Rheumatoid arthritis
COPD	Chronic obstructive pulmonary disease		RBC	Red blood count or red blood cell
CV	Cardiovascular		ROM	Range of motion
CVA	Cerebrovascular accident (stroke)		s	Without
DI	Diabetes insipidus		SBP	Systolic blood pressure
DM	Diabetes melitus		SOB	Short of breath
DOB	Date of birth		STD	Sexually transmitted diseases
Dx	Diagnosis		T	Temperature
ECG/EKG	Electrocardiogram		T&C	Type and cross-match
ENT	Ears, nose, throat		TB	Tuberculosis
ER	Emergency room		TEDS	Thrombo-embolic disease stockings
FH	Family history		TPN	Total parenteral nutrition
GERD	Gastroesophageal reflux disease		Tx	Treatment
GI	Gastrointestinal		U	Units
HA	Headache		U/A	Urinalysis
HBP	High blood pressure		UCHD	Usual childhood diseases
HDL	High density lipoprotein		URD	Upper respiratory diseases
HIV	Human immunodeficiency virus		UTI	Urinary tract infection
HR	Heart rate		VD	Venereal disease
ID	Infectious diseases		VS	Vital signs
IH	Infectious hepatitis		WBC	White blood count/cell
IO, I/O	Fluid intake and output		WT	Weight

FILL IN THE KEY TERM

Use these key terms to fill in the correct blank. Answers are at the end of the book.

anorexia	dysuria	hepatitis	prostatolith
anuria	encephalitis	hyperglycemia	pulmonary
arthritis	endocrine	hypertension	subcutaneous
blepharitis	endometriosis	lymphoma	tendinitis
bronchitis	fibromalgia	mastitis	transdermal
cardiomyopathy	gastritis	meningitis	tympanitis
colitis	hematoma	neuralgia	vasectomy
cystitis	hemophilia	onchomycosis	

1. _____ : High blood pressure.
2. _____ : Chronic pain in the muscles.
3. _____ : Inflammation of the brain.
4. _____ : Inflammation of the meninges.
5. _____ : Disease of the heart muscle.
6. _____ : Pertaining to the glands that secrete onto the bloodstream.
7. _____ : Inflammation of the joint.
8. _____ : High blood sugar.
9. _____ : Inflammation of the breast.
10. _____ : Loss of appetite.
11. _____ : Inflamed or irritable colon.
12. _____ : Inflammation of the liver from various causes.
13. _____ : Inflammation of the stomach.
14. _____ : Painful urination.
15. _____ : Beneath the skin.
16. _____ : Through the skin.
17. _____ : A collection of blood, often clotted.
18. _____ : A disease in which the blood does not clot normally.
19. _____ : Lymphatic system tumor.
20. _____ : Inability to produce urine.
21. _____ : Inflammation of a tendon.
22. _____ : Severe pain in a nerve.
23. _____ : Fungal infection of the nails.
24. _____ : Abnormal growth of uteral tissue within the pelvis.
25. _____ : Removal of a section of the vas deferens.
26. _____ : A prostate stone.
27. _____ : Inflammation of bronchial membranes.
28. _____ : Pertaining to the lungs.
29. _____ : Inflammation of the bladder.
30. _____ : Inflammation of the ear drum.
31. _____ : Inflammation of the eyelids.

CHOOSE THE BEST ANSWER

Answers are at the end of the book.

1. The system of medical and pharmaceutical nomenclature is made of these four elements:
   a. prefixes, suffixes, root words, and combining vowels.
   b. prefixes, suffixes, key words, and combining vowels.
   c. prefixes, suffixes, key words, and combining consonants.
   d. prefixes, suffixes, root words, and combining consonants.

2. The root word "xer" means
   a. around.
   b. dry.
   c. small.
   d. without.

3. Hematemesis is the vomiting of
   a. partially digested food.
   b. clear colorless liquid.
   c. blood.
   d. kidney.

4. The suffix "malacia" means
   a. treatment.
   b. tissue or structure.
   c. formation.
   d. softening.

5. Sublingual means
   a. narrowing of the tongue.
   b. inflammation of the tongue.
   c. under the tongue.
   d. without strength.

6. Prostatitis means
   a. a prostate stone.
   b. inability to produce semen.
   c. inflammation of the testes.
   d. inflammation of the prostate.

7. The primary organ of the urinary tract is the
   a. liver.
   b. kidney.
   c. bladder.
   d. intestine.

8. A keratosis is
   a. a skin inflammation.
   b. a fungal infection of the nails.
   c. an area of increased hardness.
   d. softening of the skin.

9. The suffix "megaly" means
   a. tissue.
   b. pain.
   c. enlargement.
   d. recording process.

10. The suffix "philia" means
    a. condition of.
    b. attraction for.
    c. fear of.
    d. pain.

11. Arteriosclerosis means
    a. disease of the heart.
    b. concerning heart muscle.
    c. hardening of the arteries.
    d. clotting of blood.

12. The suffix "rrhage" means
    a. to burst forth.
    b. to discharge.
    c. around.
    d. origin or production.

13. The prefix "pseudo" means
    a. halt.
    b. false.
    c. around.
    d. with.

STUDY NOTES

Use this area to write important points you'd like to remember.

— 5 —

Prescriptions

Key Concepts

Test your knowledge by covering the information in the right hand column.

prescription	A written, verbal, or electronic order from a practitioner for the preparation and administration of a medicine or a device.
prescription verification	It is necessary to check with the pharmacist on potential forgeries, on prescriptions that are more than a few days old, or on prescriptions that in any way appear questionable.
online billing	A prescription is interpreted and confirmed by the prescription system. If third party billing is involved, this is done online simultaneously.
preparation	Once the prescription and third-party billing is confirmed, the label and receipt are printed and the prescription is prepared.
label	The general purpose of the prescription label is to provide information to the patient regarding the dispensed medication and how to take it. Additionally, the label includes information about the pharmacy, the patient, the prescriber, and the prescription or transaction number assigned to the prescription. Computer-generated prescription labels must be placed on containers so they are easy to locate and easy to read.
signa	Directions for use. Since the patient is expected to self-administer the medication, these must be clear and easily understood by the patient.
pharmacist check	If a prescription has been prepared by a technician, there is a final check by the pharmacist to make sure that it is correct.
judgment questions	Technicians must request the advice of the pharmacist whenever judgment is required.

auxiliary labels

Many computerized prescription systems will automatically indicate which auxiliary labels to use with each drug.

controlled substance labels

Schedules II, III, and IV substances must carry an auxiliary label stating: "Caution: Federal law prohibits the transfer of this drug to any person other than the patient for whom it was prescribed."

institutional settings

There are different requirements for institutional prescriptions since nursing staff generally administer medications to patients. Rules for institutional pharmacy prescription labels vary by institution but often do not contain much more than the name, strength, manufacturer, expiration date, and dosage form of the medication.

medication orders

Used in institutional settings instead of a prescription form.

Health Insurance Portability and Accountability Act (HIPAA)

The Health Information Portability and Accountability Act. A federal law that protects patient privacy and regulates the sharing of protected health information.

STUDY NOTES

Use this area to write important points you'd like to remember.

COMMON PHARMACY ABBREVIATIONS

Here are the most common pharmacy abbreviations.

ROUTE

a.d.	right ear
a.s., a.l.	left ear
a.u.	each ear
i.m., IM	intramuscular
inj.	injection
i.v., IV	intravenous
i.v.p., IVP	intravenous push
IVPB	intravenous piggyback
o.d.	right eye
o.s., o.l.	left eye
o.u.	each eye
per neb	by nebulizer
p.o.	by mouth
p.r.	rectally, into the rectum
p.v.	vaginally, into the vagina
SC, subc, subq	subcutaneously
S.L.	sublingually, under the tongue
top.	topically, locally

FORM

aq, aqua	water
caps	capsules
cm	cream
elix.	elixir
liq.	liquid
supp.	suppository
SR, XR, XL	slow/extended release
syr.	syrup
tab.	tablet
ung., oint.	ointment

TIME

a.c.	before food, before meals
a.m.	morning
b.i.d.,bid	twice a day
h	hour, at the hour of
h.s.	at bedtime
p.c.	after food, after meals
p.m.	afternoon or evening
p.r.n., prn	as needed
q.i.d., qid	four times a day
q	each, every

q.d.	every day
q_h	every hour
qod	every other day
stat.	immediately
t.i.d., tid	three times a day

MEASUREMENT

$\overline{i}$	one
a.a. or aa	of each
ad	to, up to
aq. ad	add water up to
dil.	dilute
div.	divide
f, fl.	fluid
fl. oz.	fluid ounce
g., G., gm.	gram
gtt.	drop
l, L	liter/Litre
mcg.	microgram
mEq.	milliequivalent
mg.	milligram
ml., mL	milliliter/millilitre
q.s.	a sufficient quantity
q.s. ad	add sufficient quantity to make
$\overline{ss}$ or ss	one-half
tbsp.	tablespoon
tsp.	teaspoon

OTHER

c	with
disp.	dispense
f, ft.	make, let it be made
gtt	drop
NR	no refill
$\overline{s}$	without
ut dict., u.d.	as directed
sig.	write, label

Note that the use of periods in abbreviations varies greatly. It is important to be able to recognize abbreviations with or without periods.

FILL IN THE BLANK

Answers are at the end of the book.

a.a. or aa	1. _____		mEq.	32. _____
a.c.	2. _____		mg.	33. _____
a.d.	3. _____		ml.	34. _____
a.m.	4. _____		NR	35. _____
a.s.	5. _____		NS	36. _____
a.u.	6. _____		o.d.	37. _____
aq	7. _____		o.s.	38. _____
BSA	8. _____		o.u.	39. _____
bid	9. _____		p.c.	40. _____
c	10. _____		per neb	41. _____
caps	11. _____		p.o.	42. _____
per g button	12. _____		prn	43. _____
dil.	13. _____		q	44. _____
disp.	14. _____		q.d.	45. _____
per ngt	15. _____		q6h	46. _____
D5W	16. _____		qid	47. _____
elix.	17. _____		q.s.	48. _____
f, fl.	18. _____		qsad	49. _____
g., G., gm.	19. _____		$\bar{s}$	50. _____
gtt.	20. _____		SC	51. _____
h	21. _____		$\bar{\bar{ss}}$ or ss	52. _____
h.s.	22. _____		sig.	53. _____
i.m., IM	23. _____		stat.	54. _____
i.v., IV	24. _____		supp.	55. _____
i.v.p., IVP	25. _____		syr.	56. _____
NR	26. _____		tid	57. _____
IVPB	27. _____		tab.	58. _____
L.	28. _____		tbsp.	59. _____
l.	29. _____		top.	60. _____
liq.	30. _____		tsp.	61. _____
mcg.	31. _____		ung.	62. _____
			u.d.	63. _____

THE PRESCRIPTION

Prescriber information:
Name, title, office address, and telephone number

Drug Enforcement Agency (DEA) registration number of prescriber:
Required for all controlled substances

Name and address of patient:
Other patient information such as age or weight is optional but sometimes important, e.g., a child's weight.

National Provider Identifier (NPI): Prescriber's unique national identification number; required for all claims submissions effective May 23, 2007

Date: Date the prescription is written

Inscription: Name (brand or generic), strength of medication, and quantity

Refill instructions

DAW:
Dispense As Written and/or Generic Substitution Allowed instructions (optional)

Signa: This comes from the latin word signa, meaning "to write." It is abbreviated to **sig** and indicates what directions for use should be printed on the label.

Signature of prescriber:
Not required on a verbal prescription

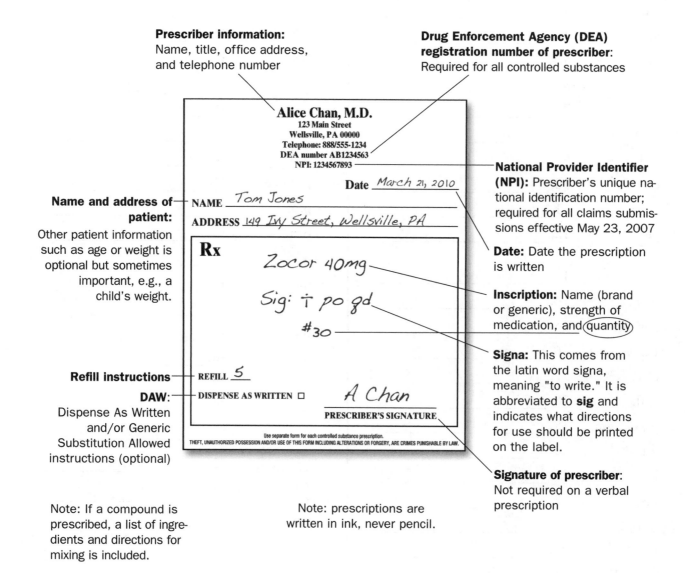

Note: If a compound is prescribed, a list of ingredients and directions for mixing is included.

Note: prescriptions are written in ink, never pencil.

PRESCRIPTION LABELS

the name, address, and telephone number of the pharmacy

the date dispensed

a prescription and/or transaction number

the name of the patient for whom the medication is dispensed

directions for use that are clear and accurate

the name, quantity, strength, manufacturer (name or NDC number), and dosage form of the medication dispensed

expiration date of the medication

the name of the prescriber

refill information.

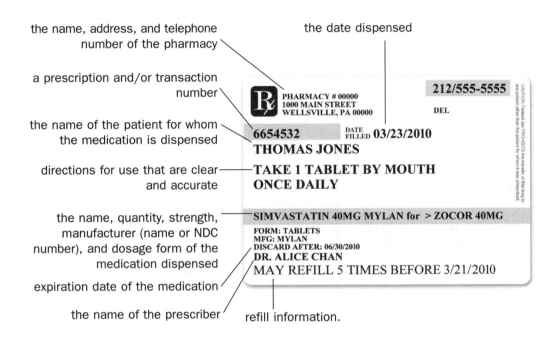

PHARMACY # 00000
1000 MAIN STREET
WELLSVILLE, PA 00000

212/555-5555

DEL

6654532   DATE FILLED **03/23/2010**

THOMAS JONES

TAKE 1 TABLET BY MOUTH ONCE DAILY

SIMVASTATIN 40MG MYLAN for > ZOCOR 40MG

FORM: TABLETS
MFG: MYLAN
DISCARD AFTER: 06/30/2010
DR. ALICE CHAN
MAY REFILL 5 TIMES BEFORE 3/21/2010

CAUTION: Federal law PROHIBITS the transfer of this drug to any person other than the patient for whom it was prescribed.

AUXILIARY LABELS

Additional, often colored auxiliary labels may also be applied to the prescription container in order to provide additional information to the patient (e.g., Shake Well, Keep Refrigerated, Take with Food or Milk). Many computerized prescription systems will automatically indicate which auxiliary labels to use.

Controlled substances from schedules II, III, and IV must carry an auxiliary label stating:

Caution: Federal law prohibits the transfer of this drug to any person other than the patient for whom it was prescribed.

TAKE WITH FOOD

TAKE MEDICATION ON AN EMPTY STOMACH

MAY CAUSE DROWSINESS

THIS DRUG MAY IMPAIR YOUR ABILITY TO DRIVE OR OPERATE MACHINERY

DO NOT DRINK ALCOHOLIC BEVERAGES WHEN TAKING THIS MEDICINE

FOR EXTERNAL USE ONLY

DO NOT TAKE ASPIRIN OR ASPIRIN CONTAINING PRODUCTS WITHOUT CONSULTING A PHYSICIAN

AVOID PROLONGED EXPOSURE TO SUNLIGHT WHILE TAKING THIS MEDICATION

PRACTICE PRESCRIPTIONS

Identify the elements on these prescriptions by answering in the space beneath the question.

Dr. A.B. Cain
123 Main Street
Wellsville, PA 00000
Telephone: 888/555-1234
DEA number AB1234563
NPI: 3333333334

Date _March 1, 2010_

NAME _D.H. Doe_

ADDRESS _345 Maple St, Wellsville PA_
_D.O.B - 2/23/54_

Rx

Prozac 20 mg

Sig: ÷ cap p.o. qd

30

REFILL _X2_

DISPENSE AS WRITTEN ☑ _A. B. Cain_

PRESCRIBER'S SIGNATURE

Use separate form for each controlled substance prescription.
THEFT, UNAUTHORIZED POSSESSION AND/OR USE OF THIS FORM INCLUDING ALTERATIONS OR FORGERY, ARE CRIMES PUNISHABLE BY LAW.

1. What is the name of the drug?

2. What is the strength?

3. What is the dosage form?

4. What is the route of administration?

5. What is the dosage?

6. How many refills are there?

7. Can there be generic substitution?

JANE T. DOE, MD
1002 Main Street
WELLSVILLE, PA, 00000
(212) 555-5555
NPI: 2222222228

Date _6/5/2010_

NAME _John Jones_

ADDRESS _____

Rx

Kenalog 0.1% Cream   15g
Apply BID

REFILL _1_

Doe

DEA No. _____

PRESCRIBER'S SIGNATURE

Use separate form for each controlled substance prescription.
THEFT, UNAUTHORIZED POSSESSION AND/OR USE OF THIS FORM INCLUDING ALTERATIONS OR FORGERY, ARE CRIMES PUNISHABLE BY LAW.

1. What is the strength of Kenalog® Cream ordered by Dr. Doe?

2. How often should the medication be applied?

PRACTICE PRESCRIPTIONS

Identify the elements on these prescriptions by answering in the space beneath the question.

JANE T. DOE, MD
1002 Main Street
WELLSVILLE, PA, 00000
(212) 555-5555
NPI: 2222222228

Date _6/5/2010_

NAME _Andrew Jones_

ADDRESS _____

Rx

Protonix 40 mg #60
T BID x 8 weeks

REFILL _1_

DEA No. _____

Doe

PRESCRIBER'S SIGNATURE

Use separate form for each controlled substance perscription
THEFT, UNAUTHORIZED POSSESSION AND/OR USE OF THIS FORM INCLUDIND ALTERATIONS OR FORGERY, ARE CRIMES PUNISHABLE BY LAW.

1. This prescription is written for Protonix®. If the medication is taken as prescribed, every day, how many days will this prescription last?

2. How many refills have been ordered for this prescription?

JANE T. DOE, MD
1002 Main Street
WELLSVILLE, PA, 00000
(212) 555-5555
NPI: 2222222228

Date _6/5/2010_

NAME _Steve Jones_

ADDRESS _____

Rx

Atrovent HFA #1 2-3 puff TID
Flovent HFA 110 mcg #1 2 puff BID

REFILL _5_

DEA No. _____

Doe

PRESCRIBER'S SIGNATURE

Use separate form for each controlled substance perscription
THEFT, UNAUTHORIZED POSSESSION AND/OR USE OF THIS FORM INCLUDIND ALTERATIONS OR FORGERY, ARE CRIMES PUNISHABLE BY LAW.

1. By reading the box for the Atrovent® HFA you find that each inhaler contains 200 inhalations. What is the days supply that should be entered in the computer for the Atrovent prescription?

2. Flovent® HFA 110 mcg is dispensed in a 12 g canister that contains 120 metered doses. What is the days supply that should be entered in the computer for the Flovent® prescription?

PRACTICE PRESCRIPTIONS

Identify the elements on these prescriptions by answering in the space beneath the question.

JANE T. DOE, MD
1002 Main Street
WELLSVILLE, PA, 00000
(212) 555-5555
NPI: 2222222228

Date __6/5/2010__

NAME __Samuel Jones__

ADDRESS _____

Rx

Synthroid 0.05 mg *DAW* #30
ⅰ po qd

REFILL __5__

Doe

DEA No. _____

PRESCRIBER'S SIGNATURE

Use separate form for each controlled substance perscription
THEFT, UNAUTHORIZED POSSESSION AND/OR USE OF THIS FORM INCLUDIND ALTERATIONS OR FORGERY, ARE CRIMES PUNISHABLE BY LAW.

1. This patient has a dual co-pay of $15 for brand and $5 for generic. The patient has requested the generic for this prescription. What is written on the prescription that does not allow the generic to be dispensed?

JANE T. DOE, MD
1002 Main Street
WELLSVILLE, PA, 00000
(212) 555-5555
NPI: 2222222228

Date __6/5/2010__

NAME __Francis Jones__

ADDRESS _____

Rx

Miacalcin 200 IU / inh
ⅰ inh qd (alt. nostrils)

REFILL __1__

Doe

DEA No. _____

PRESCRIBER'S SIGNATURE

Use separate form for each controlled substance perscription
THEFT, UNAUTHORIZED POSSESSION AND/OR USE OF THIS FORM INCLUDIND ALTERATIONS OR FORGERY, ARE CRIMES PUNISHABLE BY LAW.

1. How should the patient use this medication?

PRACTICE PRESCRIPTIONS

Identify the elements on these prescriptions by answering in the space beneath the question.

JANE T. DOE, MD
1002 Main Street
WELLSVILLE, PA, 00000
(212) 555-5555
NPI: 2222222228

Date __6/5/2010__

NAME __Sandra Jones__

ADDRESS _____

Rx

Metrogel Vaginal 70 g
T applic PV qhs x 5D

REFILL __nr__

DEA No._____

Doe

PRESCRIBER'S SIGNATURE

Use separate form for each controlled substance perscription
THEFT, UNAUTHORIZED POSSESSION AND/OR USE OF THIS FORM INCLUDIND ALTERATIONS OR FORGERY, ARE CRIMES PUNISHABLE BY LAW.

1. What does 70 g mean for this prescription?

2. What does PV mean?

JANE T. DOE, MD
1002 Main Street
WELLSVILLE, PA, 00000
(212) 555-5555
NPI: 2222222228

Date __6/5/2010__

NAME __Joyce Jones__

ADDRESS _____

Rx

Premarin 1.25 mg #21
T qd x 21, off 7

Provera 10 mg #5
1qd days 10-14

REFILL __5__

DEA No. _____

Doe

PRESCRIBER'S SIGNATURE

Use separate form for each controlled substance perscription
THEFT, UNAUTHORIZED POSSESSION AND/OR USE OF THIS FORM INCLUDIND ALTERATIONS OR FORGERY, ARE CRIMES PUNISHABLE BY LAW.

1. How many days will the Premarin® prescription last?

2. How many days will the Provera® prescription last?

PRACTICE PRESCRIPTIONS

Identify the elements on these prescriptions by answering in the space beneath the question.

JANE T. DOE, MD
1002 Main Street
WELLSVILLE, PA, 00000
(212) 555-5555
NPI: 2222222228

Date __6/5/2010__

NAME __Cindy Jones__

ADDRESS _____

Rx

Ortho-Novum 777 28 day
    T QD

REFILL __6__

DEA No. _____   __Doe__

PRESCRIBER'S SIGNATURE

Use separate form for each controlled substance perscription
THEFT, UNAUTHORIZED POSSESSION AND/OR USE OF THIS FORM INCLUDIND ALTERATIONS OR FORGERY, ARE CRIMES PUNISHABLE BY LAW.

1. What is the total number of compacts indicated by this prescription (including the original fill plus refills)?

JANE T. DOE, MD
1002 Main Street
WELLSVILLE, PA, 00000
(212) 555-5555
NPI: 2222222228

Date __6/5/2010__

NAME __Jane Jones__

ADDRESS _____

Rx

Bactrim DS 20
    T po BID

REFILL __nr__

DEA No. _____   __Doe__

PRESCRIBER'S SIGNATURE

Use separate form for each controlled substance perscription
THEFT, UNAUTHORIZED POSSESSION AND/OR USE OF THIS FORM INCLUDIND ALTERATIONS OR FORGERY, ARE CRIMES PUNISHABLE BY LAW.

1. As you are entering this prescription in the computer, an allergy warning is displayed on the computer screen. What type of allergy does Jane Jones have?

PRACTICE PRESCRIPTIONS

Identify the elements on these prescriptions by answering in the space beneath the question.

JANE T. DOE, MD
1002 Main Street
WELLSVILLE, PA, 00000
(212) 555-5555
NPI: 2222222228

Date _6/5/2010_

NAME _Ann Jones_

ADDRESS _____

Rx

Lorabid 200 mg/5 ml
i₃ po BID x 10

REFILL _nr_

Doe

DEA No. _____

PRESCRIBER'S SIGNATURE

Use separate form for each controlled substance perscription
THEFT, UNAUTHORIZED POSSESSION AND/OR USE OF THIS FORM INCLUDIND ALTERATIONS OR FORGERY, ARE CRIMES PUNISHABLE BY LAW.

1. What directions should be placed on the label for this prescription?

JANE T. DOE, MD
1002 Main Street
WELLSVILLE, PA, 00000
(212) 555-5555
NPI: 2222222228

Date _6/5/2010_

NAME _Tom Jones_

ADDRESS _____

Rx

Amoxicillin 500 mg 2 po BID x 7
Biaxin 500 mg po BID x 7
Aciphex 20 mg po BID x 7

REFILL _nr_

Doe

DEA No. _____

PRESCRIBER'S SIGNATURE

Use separate form for each controlled substance perscription
THEFT, UNAUTHORIZED POSSESSION AND/OR USE OF THIS FORM INCLUDIND ALTERATIONS OR FORGERY, ARE CRIMES PUNISHABLE BY LAW.

1. How many capsules should be dispensed for the amoxicillin?

2. How many tablets should be dispensed for the Biaxin®?

3. How many tablets should be dispensed for the Aciphex®?

PRACTICE MEDICATION ORDERS

Identify the elements on this medication order by answering in the space beneath the question.

		PATIENT IDENTIFICATION	
DOCTOR'S ORDERS		099999999 675-01 SMITH, JOHN 12/06/1950 DR. P. JOHNSON	

DATE	TIME	**DOCTOR'S ORDERS 1**	DATE/TIME INITIALS	DATE/TIME INITIALS
1/3/10	2200	Admit patient to 6th floor		
		Pneumonia, Dehydration		
		All: PCN- Rash		
		Order CBC, chem-7, blood cultures stat		
		NS @ 125ml/hr IV		
		Dr Johnson X2222		

DATE	TIME	**DOCTOR'S ORDERS 2**	DATE/TIME INITIALS	DATE/TIME INITIALS
2/01/10	300	Tylenol 650mg po q4-6 hrs PRN for Temp>38°C		
		Verbal Order Dr Johnson/ Jane Doe, RN		

DATE	TIME	**DOCTOR'S ORDERS 3**	DATE/TIME INITIALS	DATE/TIME INITIALS
2/01/10	600	Start Clarithromycin 500mg po q 12°		
		Multivitamin po qd		
		Order CXR for this a.m		
		Dr Johnson X2222		

1. What is the patient's disorder/condition?

2. Does the patient have allergies?

3. What route and dosage is ordered for the Tylenol® 650 mg?

4. What orders did the physician sign for?

5. What route and dosage are prescribed for the Clarithromycin?

6. What route and dosage are prescribed for the multivitamin?

PRACTICE MEDICATION ORDERS

Identify the elements on this medication order by answering in the space beneath the question.

PATIENT:	John Smith	CITY HOSPITAL
AGE:	35	
SEX:	m	PHYSICIAN'S ORDERS
CHART #:	#123555	

ALLERGIES:

DIAGNOSIS:

COMPLETED OR DISCONTINUED

DATE	TIME	ORDERS	SIGNATURE	NAME	DATE	TIME
		Meds:				
6/5/10	12:34 pm	① Lopressor 50 mg po qd				
		② HCTZ 25 mg po qd				
		③ Sonata 5 mg po hs prn				
		Doe				

PHARMACY COPY

1. What three medications have been ordered?

2. How often should the Sonata® be taken?

PRACTICE MEDICATION ORDERS

Identify the elements on these medication orders by answering in the space beneath the question.

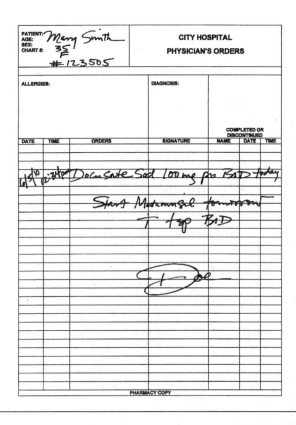

1. What medication has been ordered for today?

2. What medication should be started tomorrow?

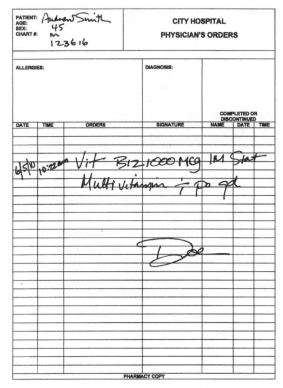

1. What does STAT mean in the order for Vitamin B-12?

2. What is the route of administration for Vitamin B-12?

PRACTICE MEDICATION ORDERS

Identify the elements on these medication orders by answering in the space beneath the question.

PATIENT: Steve Smith		CITY HOSPITAL
AGE: 45 SEX: m CHART #: 1 23777		PHYSICIAN'S ORDERS

ALLERGIES: Penicillin		DIAGNOSIS:			
			COMPLETED OR DISCONTINUED		
DATE	TIME	ORDERS	SIGNATURE	NAME	DATE	TIME

6/5/10 10:15ᵃᵐ IVF NS @ 100 cc/hr x2 l
HCTZ 25 mg po qd
Diovan 80 mg po qd
Doe

PHARMACY COPY

1. What is the rate for the IV in this medication order?

2. What medications are to be given orally?

PATIENT: Barbara Smith		CITY HOSPITAL
AGE: 45 SEX: F CHART #: 123718		PHYSICIAN'S ORDERS

ALLERGIES: Codeine		DIAGNOSIS:			
			COMPLETED OR DISCONTINUED		
DATE	TIME	ORDERS	SIGNATURE	NAME	DATE	TIME

6/5/10 10:10ᵃᵐ FS AC + HS
Micronase 5mg po qd
Ambien 5mg po hs prn
Doe

PHARMACY COPY

1. What medications have been ordered?

2. Which medication would be administered at bedtime, as needed?

53

FILL IN THE KEY TERM

Use these key terms to fill in the correct blank. Answers are at the end of the book.

auxiliary label	**HIPAA**	**PHI**
DAW	**institutional labels**	**prescription**
DEA number	**look-alikes**	**Rx**
DUR	**medication order**	**Signa**
extemporaneous compounding	**NPI**	

1. _____ : A written order from a practitioner for the preparation and administration of a medicine or a device.

2. _____ : The pharmaceutical preparation of a medication from ingredients.

3. _____ : Health Insurance Portability and Accountability Act that requires pharmacies to provide written notice of their privacy practices.

4. _____ : The directions for use on a prescription that should be printed on the label.

5. _____ : The additional warning labels that are placed on filled prescription containers.

6. _____ : The form used to prescribe medications for patients in institutional settings.

7. _____ : Drug names that have similar appearance, particularly when written.

8. _____ : Abbreviation for the Latin word "recipe."

9. _____ : Dispense As Written, meaning generic substitution not allowed.

10. _____ : Protected health information defined under HIPAA.

11. _____ : Often do not contain much more than the name, strength, manufacturer, expiration date, and dosage form of the medication.

12. _____ : Drug utilization review.

13. _____ : Prescriber's unique national identification number.

14. _____ : Required on all controlled substance prescriptions.

TRUE/FALSE

Indicate whether the statement is true or false in the blank. Answers are at the end of the book.

_____ 1. In addition to the primary prescribers, nurse practitioners and physician assistants are allowed to write prescriptions in some states.

_____ 2. Prescriptions may be handwritten or electronically produced.

_____ 3. The signa indicates the medication and its strength.

_____ 4. If DAW is indicated, generic substitution may not be used.

_____ 5. A prescription has no time limit.

_____ 6. Counseling patients on the use of OTC medications should be done by the pharmacist.

_____ 7. One of the primary purposes of the prescription label is to provide the patient with clear instructions on how to take the medication.

_____ 8. Institutional labels must have the same information as in the community setting.

_____ 9. The prescription label may have either the date dispensed or the expiration date, but does not need both.

_____ 10. A DEA number is required on all prescriptions.

EXPLAIN WHY

Explain why these statements are true or important. Check your answers in the text. Discuss any questions you may have with your Instructor.

1. Why must the pharmacist always check the filled prescription before it is dispensed to the patient?

2. Why must the directions for use be clear and understandable to the patient in the community setting?

3. What are the differences between the prescription and the medication order? Why?

4. Why must prescriptions be written in ink?

5. Why are auxiliary labels important?

CHOOSE THE BEST ANSWER

Answers are at the end of the book.

1. A prescription was written for Zocor® and Simvastatin was dispensed in accordance with insurance plan guidelines. This is an example of
   a. D.A.W.
   b. look-alike.
   c. generic substitution.
   d. prior authorization.

2. In community pharmacies, _____ generally receive the prescription and collect patient data and enter this information into the computer.
   a. pharmacists
   b. pharmacy technicians

3. In institutional settings, _____ generally administer medications to patients.
   a. nursing staff
   b. pharmacy staff

4. When a prescription is written for a medication that is not commercially available, the medication can be prepared by mixing the ingredients required and this is called
   a. alligation.
   b. extemporaneous compounding.
   c. trituration.
   d. admixture.

5. If a new prescription has been prepared by a pharmacy technician, the final check is done by the
   a. lead pharmacy technician.
   b. pharmacist.
   c. patient.
   d. physician.

6. Prescriptions are written in
   a. ink.
   b. either ink or pencil.
   c. pencil.

7. The DEA Number is required on prescriptions for
   a. legend drugs.
   b. medical devices.
   c. controlled substances.
   d. OTCs.

8. The name of the drug, its strength, and quantity make up the
   a. insigna.
   b. signa.
   c. inscription.
   d. DAW indicator.

9. PSC stands for
   a. prescription safety code.
   b. prescription signa code.
   c. product select code.
   d. profile safety code.

10. The route of administration should be indicated on the prescription if it is different from
    a. injectable.
    b. rectal.
    c. oral.
    d. topical.

11. When the Sig contains t.i.d., the medication should be taken _____ times a day.
    a. one
    b. two
    c. three
    d. four

12. Labels from _____ pharmacies contain more information than labels from _____ pharmacies.
    a. community, institutional
    b. institutional, hospital
    c. institutional, community
    d. hospital, institutional

CHOOSE THE BEST ANSWER

Answers are at the end of the book.

13. If a prescription requires extemporaneous compounding, the technician should inform the patient that
    a. the medication may be obtained without a prescription.
    b. there may be a delay in filling the prescription.
    c. a DEA number is required.
    d. any refills cannot be honored.

14. Directions should start with a
    a. verb.
    b. noun.
    c. adjective.
    d. pronoun.

15. For the prescription: Bactrim® DS #20 ī b.i.d. nr, how many days should the prescription last?
    a. 2
    b. 5
    c. 10
    d. 20

STUDY NOTES

Use this area to write important points you'd like to remember.

— 6 —

Calculations

RATIO AND PROPORTION

Most of the calculations pharmacy technicians will face on the job or in the certification exam can be performed using the ratio and proportion method.

A ratio states a relationship between two quantities. ➡ $\frac{a}{b}$

A proportion contains two equal ratios. ➡ $\frac{a}{b} = \frac{c}{d}$

When three of the four quantities in a proportion are known, the value of the fourth (x) can be easily solved. ➡ $\frac{x}{b} = \frac{c}{d}$

CONDITIONS FOR USING RATIO AND PROPORTION

1. Three of the four values must be known.

2. Numerators must have the same units.

3. Denominators must have the same units.

STEPS FOR SOLVING PROPORTION PROBLEMS

1. Define the variable and correct ratios.

2. Set-up the proportion equation.

3. Establish the x equation.

4. Solve for x.

5. Express the solution in correct units.

Example

If there are 125 mg of a substance in a 500 ml solution, and 50 mg is desired, the amount of solution needed can be determined with this equation:

$$\frac{x \text{ ml}}{50 \text{ mg}} = \frac{500 \text{ ml}}{125 \text{ mg}}$$

multiplying both sides by 50 mg gives:

$$x \text{ ml} = 2500 \text{ ml}/125$$

solving for x gives:

$$x = 200$$

answer: 200 ml of solution are needed.

CONVERSIONS

Many proportion problems involve the use of conversions from one unit of measure to another. Here is a list of the most common.

Liquid Metric

1 L	=	10 dl	=	1000 ml
1 dl	=	0.1 L	=	100 ml
1 ml	=	0.001 L	=	0.01 dl

Solid Metric

1 kg	=	1,000 g		
1 g	=	0.001 kg	=	1,000 mg
1 mg	=	0.001 g	=	1,000 mcg
1 mcg	=	0.001 mg		

Avoirdupois

1 lb	=	16 oz
1 oz	=	437.5 gr
1 gr	=	64.8 mg (.0648 g)

Apothecary

1 gal	=	4 qt
1 qt	=	2 pt
1 pt	=	16 fl oz
1 fl oz	=	8 fl dr
1 fl dr	=	60 m

Household

1 tsp	=	5 ml		
1 tbs	=	3 tsp	=	15 ml
1 cup	=	8 fl oz		

Temperature

F temperature $= (1\frac{4}{5}$ times number of degrees C) + 32

C temperature $= \frac{5}{9}$ x (number of degrees F - 32)

9C = 5F - 16

Conversions Between Systems

1 L	=	33.8 fl oz		1 lb	=	453.59 g
1 pt	=	473.167 ml		1 oz	=	28.35 g
1 fl oz	=	29.57ml		1 g	=	15.43 gr
1 kg	=	2.2 lb		1 gr	=	64.8 mg

ROMAN NUMERALS

Roman numerals can be capital or lower case letters, and are:

ss = 1/2	L or l = 50
I or i = 1	C or c = 100
V or v = 5	D or d = 500
X or x = 10	M or m = 1000

RULES:

➡ When the second of two letters has a value equal to or smaller than that of the first, their values are to be added.

➡ When the second of two letters has a value greater than that of the first, the smaller is to be subtracted from the larger.

CONVERSION EXERCISES

Convert these numbers to decimals:

1. 5/8 _____
2. 0.2% _____
3. 1/4 _____
4. 2/3 _____
5. 12% _____
6. 42.5% _____
7. 3.2% _____

Write the following in Roman numerals:

15. 67 _____
16. 29 _____
17. 71 _____
18. 108 _____
19. 8 _____
20. 98 _____
21. 9 _____

Convert these numbers to percents:

8. 0.7 _____
9. 75/100 _____
10. 1.5 _____
11. 1/8 _____
12. 0.075 _____
13. 4/5 _____
14. 0.025 _____

Write the following in arabic numbers:

22. XIX _____
23. CIII _____
24. CMM _____
25. iiss _____
26. XXX _____
27. LIV _____

PROBLEMS

1. You have a prescription that calls for 1 cap po qid x 10 days. How many capsules are needed?

2. You have a prescription that calls for 1 cap po tid x 14 days. How many capsules are needed?

3. If a compounding order calls for Flagyl® 125 mg bid x 7 days, and only 500 mg tablets are available, how many tablets will it take to fill the order?

4. How much talc is needed for an order for 120 gm of the following compound: Nupercainal® ointment 4%, zinc oxide 20%, talc 2%?

5. A prescription calls for 200 mg of a drug that you have in a 10 mg/15 ml concentration. How many ml of the liquid do you need?

PEDIATRIC DOSES

Because of the many variables, conversion formulas for pediatric doses are rarely used in the pharmacy. Doses are generally given by the physician. **Children's doses are stated by kg of body weight (dose/kg).** Since 1 kg = 2.2 lb, you can solve for the prescribed dose by using a proportion equation if you know the child's body weight. See the following example.

An antibiotic IV is prescribed for an infant. The dose is to be 15 mg/kg twice a day. The baby weighs 12 lbs. How much drug is to be given for one dose? First the infant's weight in kilograms should be calculated.

$$x \text{ kg} / 12 \text{ lb} = 1 \text{ kg} / 2.2 \text{ lb}$$

$$x \text{ kg} = 12 \text{ lb} \text{ times } \frac{1 \text{ kg}}{2.2 \text{ lb}} = \frac{12 \text{ kg}}{2.2} = 5.45 \text{ kg}$$

The next part of this problem can be solved with a simple equation.

$$\text{one dose} = 15 \text{ mg times } 5.45 = 81.75 \text{ mg}$$

PERCENTS & SOLUTIONS

Percents are used to indicate the amount or **concentration** of something in a solution. Concentrations are indicated in terms of weight to volume or volume to volume. The standard units are:

Weight to Volume: grams per 100 milliliters ➡ g/100 ml

Volume to Volume: milliliters per 100 milliliters ➡ mL/100 ml

A PERCENT SOLUTION FORMULA

Technicians find that they often have to convert a solution at one concentration to a solution having a different concentration, especially during the preparation of hyperalimentation or TPNs. It is possible to make such conversions using a simple proportion equation with these elements:

$$\frac{x \text{ volume wanted}}{\text{want \%}} = \frac{\text{volume prescribed}}{\text{have \%}}$$

FLOW RATE

In some settings, the flow rate or rate of administration for an IV solution needs to be calculated. This is done using a ratio and proportion equation. Rates are generally calculated in ml/hour, but for pumps used to dispense IV fluids to a patient, the calculation may need to be done in ml/min or gtt/min.

For example, if you have an order for KCl 10 mEq and K Acetate 15 mEq in D5W 1000 ml to run at 80 ml/hour, you would determine the administration rate in ml/minute as follows:

x ml / 1 min = 80 ml / 60 min

x = 80/60 = 1.33

To get **drops per minute (gtt/min)**, you must have a conversion rate of drops per ml. For example, if the administration set for the above order delivered 30 drops per ml, you would find the drops per minute as follows:

$$\frac{80 \text{ ml}}{60 \text{ min}} \times \frac{30 \text{ gtt}}{1 \text{ ml}} = \frac{2400 \text{ gtt}}{60 \text{ min}} = 40 \text{ gtt/min}$$

MILLIEQUIVALENTS—MEQ

Electrolytes are substances which conduct an electrical current and are found in the body's blood, tissue fluids, and cells. Salts are electrolytes and saline solutions are a commonly used electrolyte solution. The concentration of electrolytes in a volume of solution is measured in units called milliequivalents (mEq). They are expressed as milliequivalents per milliliter or equivalents per liter.

Milliequivalents are a unit of measurement specific to each electrolyte. For example, a 0.9% solution of one electrolyte will have a different mEq value than a 0.9% solution of another because mEq values are based on each electrolyte's atomic weight and electron properties, each of which is different.

If the mEq value of a solution is known, it is relatively easy to mix it with other solutions to get a different mEq volume ratio by using proportions.

EXAMPLE

A solution calls for 5 mEq of an electrolyte that you have in a 1.04 mEq/ml solution. How many ml of it do you need?

x ml/5 mEq = 1 ml/1.04 mEq

$$\textbf{x} \text{ ml} = 5 \text{ mEq times } \frac{1 \text{ ml}}{1.04 \text{ mEq}} = \frac{5 \text{ ml}}{1.04} = 4.8 \text{ ml}$$

Answer: 4.8 ml of the solution is needed.

PROBLEMS

6.   An IV requires the addition of 40 mEq potassium chloride (KCl). You have a vial of KCl at a concentration of 20 mEq per 10 ml. How many ml should be added?

7.   If 200 grams of dextrose is ordered using a 50% dextrose solution, how many ml are needed?

8.   A prescription calls for 0.36 mg of a drug that you have in 50 mcg/ml concentration. How many ml do you need?

9.   The infusion rate of an IV is 300 ml over 5 hours. What is the ml/minute rate?

10.   The infusion rate of an IV is 1000 ml over 12 hours. What is the rate in ml per minute?

11. An IV order calls for administration of 1.5 ml/minute of a solution for four hours. How much solution will be needed.

12. If a physician orders 25% dextrose 1000 ml and all you have is 70% dextrose 1000 ml, how much 70% dextrose and how much sterile water will be used?

13. If a physician orders 20% dextrose 1000 ml and all you have is 70% dextrose 1000 ml, how much 70% dextrose and how much sterile water will be used?

14. If a physician orders 25% dextrose 500 ml and you have 50% dextrose 1000 ml, how much 50% dextrose and how much sterile water do you need?

TOTAL PARENTERAL NUTRITION

A TPN order calls for the amounts on the left (including additives) to be made from the items on the right. The total volume is to be 1000 ml. How much of each ingredient and how much sterile water do you need to prepare this TPN?

TPN Order	On Hand	
Aminosyn® 4.25%	Aminosyn® 8.5%	1000 ml
dextrose 20%	dextrose 50%	500 ml

Additives:

KCl	24 mEq	KCl 2mEq/ml	20 ml
MVI	5 ml	MVI	10 ml
NaCl	24 mEq	NaCl 4.4mEq/ml	20 ml

Figure out the amounts and enter the answer on the blank line.

1. Aminosyn® _____

2. dextrose _____

3. KCl _____

4. MVI _____

5. NaCl _____

6. sterile water _____

RETAIL MATH

Technicians in community pharmacies must know how to perform common retail calculations. Besides simple addition and subtraction, the most important calculations involve using percentages, especially in doing mark-ups or discounts. A mark-up is the amount of the retailer's selling price minus their purchase cost. It is calculated by multiplying the retailer's purchase cost by the mark-up percentage and adding the amount to the cost.

For example, a 30% mark-up on an item purchased for $2.30 is $0.69 (Note that 30% equals 0.3, and that $2.30 x 0.3 = $0.69), so the selling price would be $2.99 ($2.30 + $0.69).

Conversely, if you knew a $2.99 sale item was marked-up $0.69 and were asked to figure out the percent mark-up, you would subtract the $0.69 from $2.99 to get the cost of the item ($2.30), and then divide the mark-up by the cost: $0.69 ÷ $2.30 = 0.3 = 30%.

Discounts involve subtracting a percentage amount from the marked-up price of an item. A 30% discount on the $2.99 item is $0.90, so $2.09 would be the discounted price ($2.99-$0.90). Note that this is different than the cost of the item, because you deducted the percentage from the marked-up price.

— 7 —

ROUTES & FORMULATIONS

KEY CONCEPTS

Test your knowledge by covering the information in the right hand column.

formulations

Drugs are contained in products called formulations. There are many drug formulations and many different routes to administer them.

route of administration

Routes are classified as enteral or parenteral. Enteral refers to anything involving the tract from the mouth to the rectum. There are three enteral routes: oral, sublingual, and rectal. Any route other than oral, sublingual, and rectal is considered a parenteral administration route. Oral administration is the most frequently used route of administration.

local and systemic effects

A local effect occurs when the drug activity is at the site of administration (e.g., eyes, ears, nose, skin). A systemic effect occurs when the drug is introduced into the circulatory system.

oral administration

The stomach has a pH around 1–2. Certain drugs cannot be taken orally because they are degraded or destroyed by stomach acid and intestinal enzymes. Drugs administered by liquid dosage forms generally reach the circulatory system faster than drugs formulated in solid dosage forms.

oral formulations

Oral formulations contain various ingredients beside the active drug. These inactive ingredients include binders, lubricants, fillers, diluents, and disintegrants.

gastrointestinal action

The disintegration and dissolution of tablets, capsules, and powders generally begins in the stomach, but will continue to occur when the stomach empties into the intestine. Modified-release formulations extend dissolution over a period of hours and provide a longer duration of effect compared to plain tablets. Enteric coated tablets prevent the tablet from disintegrating until it reaches the higher pHs of the intestine.

sublingual administration	These tablets are placed under the tongue. They are generally fast dissolving uncoated tablets which contain highly water soluble drugs. When the drug is released from the tablet, it is quickly absorbed into the circulatory system since the membranes lining the mouth are very thin and there is a rich blood supply to the mouth.
rectal administration	Rectal administration may be used to achieve a variety of systemic effects, including: asthma control, antinausea, anti-motion sickness, and anti-infective. However, absorption from rectal administration is erratic and unpredictable. The most common rectal administration forms are suppositories, solutions, and ointments.
parenteral administration	Parenteral routes are often preferred when oral administration causes drug degradation or when a rapid drug response is desired, as in an emergency situation. The parenteral routes requiring a needle are intravenous, intramuscular, intradermal, and subcutaneous. These solutions must be sterile (bacteria-free), have an appropriate pH, and be limited in volume.
intravenous formulations	Intravenous dosage forms are administered directly into a vein (and the blood supply). Most solutions are aqueous (water based), but they may also have glycols, alcohols, or other non-aqueous solvents in them.
IV emulsions	Fat emulsions and TPN emulsions are used to provide triglycerides, fatty acids, and calories for patients who cannot absorb them from the gastrointestinal tract.
infusion	Infusion is the gradual intravenous injection of a volume of fluid into a patient.
intravenous sites	Several sites on the body are used to intravenously administer drugs: the veins of the antecubital area (in front of the elbow), the back of the hand, and some of the larger veins in the foot. On some occasions, a vein must be exposed by a surgical cut.
intramuscular injections	The principal sites of injection are the gluteal maximus (buttocks), deltoid (upper arm), and vastus lateralis (thigh) muscles. Intramuscular injections generally result in lower but longer lasting blood concentrations than with intravenous administration.
subcutaneous injections	Injection sites include the back of the upper arm, the front of the thigh, the lower portion of the abdomen and the upper back. The subcutaneous (SC, SQ) route can be used for both short term and very long term therapies. Insulin is the most important drug routinely administered by this route.

KEY CONCEPTS

Test your knowledge by covering the information in the right hand column.

intradermal injections	Intradermal injections involve small volumes that are injected into the top layer of skin. The usual site for intradermal injections is the anterior surface of the forearm.
ophthalmic formulations	Every ophthalmic product must be manufactured to be sterile in its final container. A major problem of ophthalmic administration is the immediate loss of a dose by natural spillage from the eye.
intranasal formulations	Intranasal formulations are primarily used for their decongestant activity on the nasal mucosa, the cellular lining of the nose. The drugs that are typically used are decongestants, antihistamines, and corticosteroids. Nasal administration often causes amounts of the drug to be swallowed, in some cases this may lead to a systemic effect.
inhalation formulations	Inhalation dosage forms are intended to deliver drugs to the pulmonary system (lungs). Most of the inhalation dosage forms are aerosols that depend on the power of compressed or liquefied gas to expel the drug from the container. Gaseous or volatile anesthetics are the most important drugs administered via this route. Other drugs administered affect lung function, act as bronchodilators, or treat allergic symptoms. Examples of drugs administered by this route are adrenocorticoid steroids (beclomethasone), bronchodilators (epinephrine, isoproterenol, metaproterenol, albuterol), and antiallergics (cromolyn sodium).
dermal formulations	Most dermal dosage forms are used for local (topical) effects on or within the skin. Dermal formulations are used to treat minor skin infections, itching, burns, diaper rash, insect stings and bites, athlete's foot, corns, calluses, warts, dandruff, acne, psoriasis, and eczema. The major disadvantage of this route of administration is that the amount of drug that can be absorbed will be limited to about 2 mg/hour.
vaginal administration	Formulations for this route of administration are: solutions, powders for solutions, ointments, creams, aerosol foams, suppositories, tablets, and IUDs. Vaginal administration leads to variable absorption since the vagina is a physiologically and anatomically dynamic organ with pH and absorption characteristics changing over time. Another disadvantage of this route is that administration of a formulation during menstruation could predispose the patient to Toxic Shock Syndrome.

TRUE/FALSE

Indicate whether the statement is true or false in the blank. Answers are at the end of the book.

_____ 1.   Buccal administration is a parenteral route of administration.

_____ 2.   Oral administration is the most frequently used route of administration.

_____ 3.   With oral formulations, drugs administered by solid dosage forms generally reach the systemic circulation faster than liquid dosage forms.

_____ 4.   A low pH value such as 1 or 2 indicates a high acidity.

_____ 5.   Parenteral administration always involves the use of a needle.

_____ 6.   Phlebitis can be a complication of intravenous administration.

_____ 7.   Aqueous solutions are water-based.

_____ 8.   Insulin is routinely administered by the subcutaneous route.

_____ 9.   Ophthalmic ointment tubes typically hold about 3.5 g of ointment.

_____ 10. Toxic shock syndrome is a disease caused by a bacterial infection.

EXPLAIN WHY

Explain why these statements are true or important. Check your answers in the text. Discuss any questions you may have with your Instructor.

1.   Give three reasons why a drug might not be used for oral administration.

2.   Give three reasons why a drug might not be used for parenteral administration.

3.   Why do most parenterals require skilled personnel to administer them?

4.   Why is the pH of intravenous solutions important?

5.   Why is the development of infusion pumps important?

6.   Why is a spacer sometimes used with a metered-dose inhaler?

FILL IN THE KEY TERM

Answers are at the end of the book.

alveoli
atomizer
buccal cavity
buffer system
bulk powders
conjunctiva
contraceptive
elastomeric pump
elixirs
emulsions
enteric coated
hemorrhoid
inactive ingredients
inspiration

intradermal injections
intramuscular injection sites
intravenous sites
IUD
lacrimal canalicula
lacrimal gland
local effect
metered dose inhalers
nasal inhaler
nasal mucosa
necrosis
ophthalmic
parenteral
percutaneous

pH
solvent
sterile
subcutaneous injection sites
sublingual administration
syrups
systemic effect
Toxic Shock Syndrome
transcorneal transport
viscosity
water soluble
wheal
Z-tract injection

1. _____ : When the drug activity is at the site of administration (e.g., eyes, ears, nose, skin).

2. _____ : When a drug is introduced into the circulatory system by any route of administration and carried to the site of activity.

3. _____ : Ingredients designed to control the pH of a product.

4. _____ : Solid formulations to be mixed with water or juice.

5. _____ : The pouch between the cheeks and teeth.

6. _____ : Ingredients beside the active drug that include binders, effervescent salts, lubricants, fillers, diluents, and disintegrants.

7. _____ : Coating that will not let the tablet disintegrate until it reaches the higher pHs of the intestine.

8. _____ : The property of a substance being able to dissolve in water.

9. _____ : When tablets are placed under the tongue.

10. _____ : Measure of acidity or alkalinity of a substance.

11. _____ : Any route that does not involve the alimentary tract.

12. _____ : Increase in cell death.

13. _____ : Related to the eye.

14. _____ : Injections administered into the top layer of the skin using short needles.

15. _____ : The veins of the antecubital area (in front of the elbow), the back of the hand, and some of the larger veins in the foot.

16. _____ : Painful/swollen veins in the anal/rectal area.

17. _____ : A liquid that dissolves another substance in it.

18. _____ : Tear ducts.

19. _____ : Drug transfer into the eye.

20. _____ : A mixture of two liquids that do not mix with each other in which one liquid is spread through the other by mixing and use of a stabilizer.

21. _____ : Gluteal (buttocks), deltoid (upper arm), and vastus lateralis (thigh) muscles.

22. _____ : The back of the upper arm, the front of the thigh, the lower portion of the abdomen and the upper back.

23. _____ : The thickness of a liquid.

24. _____ : Small sacs of tissue that transfer oxygen.

25. _____ : A raised blister-like area on the skin, as caused by an intradermal injection.

26. _____ : The gland that produces tears for the eye.

27. _____ : Intravenous devices for intermittent or very slow continuous infusions.

28. _____ : The eyelid lining.

29. _____ : Injection technique for medications that stain the skin.

30. _____ : The cellular lining of the nose.

31. _____ : Device used to convert liquid to a spray.

32. _____ : A device which contains a drug that is vaporized by inhalation.

33. _____ : Breathing in.

34. _____ : Aerosols that use special metering valves to deliver a fixed dose when the aerosol is actuated.

35. _____ : The absorption of drugs through the skin, often for a systemic effect.

36. _____ : Hydroalcoholic liquids for oral use.

37. _____ : Concentrated solutions of sugar in water.

38. _____ : Free of microrganisms.

39. _____ : A rare and potentially fatal disease that results from a severe bacterial infection of the blood.

40. _____ : A device or formulation designed to prevent pregnancy.

41. _____ : An intrauterine contraceptive device that is placed in the uterus for a prolonged period of time.

IDENTIFY

Identify the route of administration.

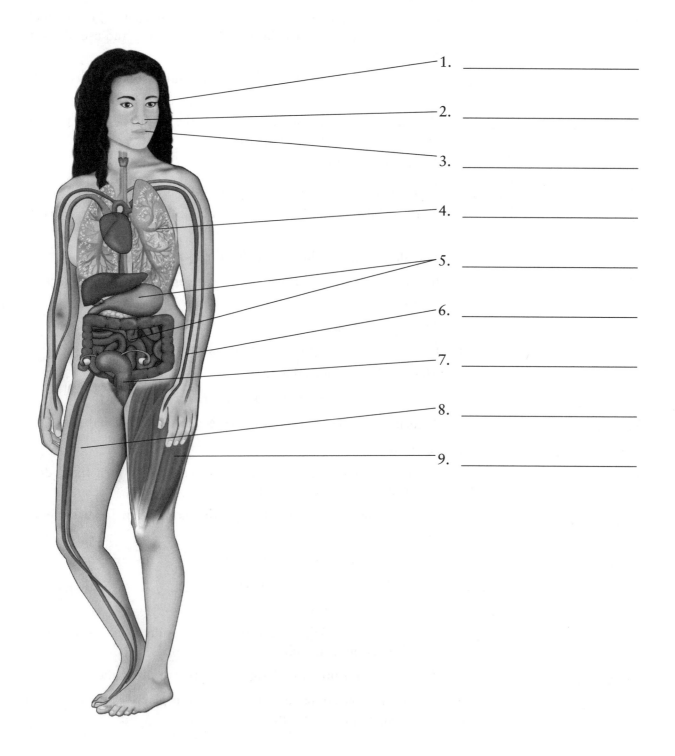

1. _____

2. _____

3. _____

4. _____

5. _____

6. _____

7. _____

8. _____

9. _____

IDENTIFY

Identify the routes of administration.

1. _____

2. _____

3. _____

4. _____

Identify these sites of intramuscular administration on the figure at right:

1. deltoid   _____
2. gluteus maximus   _____
3. gluteus medius   _____
4. vastus lateralis   _____
5. ventrogluteal   _____

CHOOSE THE BEST ANSWER

Answers are at the end of the book.

1. _____ tablets are placed under the tongue.
   a. Enteric coated
   b. Buccal
   c. Sublingual
   d. TSS

2. The pH of the stomach is around
   a. 1–2.
   b. 4–5.
   c. 5–6.
   d. 6–7.

3. _____ injections are administered directly into veins.
   a. Subcutaneous
   b. Intravenous
   c. Transdermal
   d. Intramuscular

4. Inflammation of a vein is also known as _____ and can be a complication associated with intravenous administration.
   a. thrombus
   b. toxic shock
   c. phlebitis
   d. embolus

5. The gradual intravenous injection of a volume of fluid into a patient is called
   a. transdermal.
   b. infiltration.
   c. infusion.
   d. suspension.

6. The maximum amount of medication that can be administered subcutaneously is
   a. 0.5 ml.
   b. 2 ml.
   c. 0.2 ml.
   d. 5 ml.

7. _____ contain the drug and other ingredients packaged in a gelatin shell.
   a. Tablets
   b. Capsules
   c. Emulsions
   d. Gels

8. The normal volume of tears in the eye is estimated to be
   a. 7 microliters.
   b. 2 ml.
   c. 5 ml.
   d. 3 ml.

9. The normal commercial eyedropper dispenses _____ of solution.
   a. 50 microliters
   b. 2 ml
   c. 1 ml
   d. 0.5 ml

10. A device that goes between an aerosol's mouthpiece and the patient's mouth is a/an
    a. atomizer.
    b. nebulizer.
    c. spacer.
    d. MDI.

11. MDIs are used to deliver drugs by
    a. inhalation.
    b. infusion.
    c. injection.

12. _____ absorption is the absorption of drugs through the skin, often for systemic effect.
    a. Intravenous
    b. Intramuscular
    c. Subcutaneous
    d. Percutaneous

13. The most common injection route for insulin is
    a. subcutaneous.
    b. intramuscular.
    c. sublingual.
    d. intradermal.

14. Pastes are generally used for their _____ action.
    a. lubricating
    b. cooling
    c. heating
    d. protective

STUDY NOTES

Use this area to write important points you'd like to remember.

— 8 —

PARENTERALS: STERILE FORMULATIONS

KEY CONCEPTS

Test your knowledge by covering the information in the right hand column.

parenteral solutions

There are two types of products: large volume parenteral (LVP) solutions and small volume parenteral (SVP) solutions. LVP solutions are typically bags or bottles containing larger volumes of intravenous solutions. SVP solutions are generally contained in ampules or vials.

properties

Solutions for injection or infusion must be sterile, free of visible particulate material, pyrogen-free, stable for their intended use, have a pH around 7.4, and in most (but not all) cases isotonic.

admixtures

When a drug is added to a parenteral solution, the drug is referred to as the additive, and the final mixture is referred to as the admixture.

total parenteral nutrition solutions

These are complex admixtures composed of dextrose, fat, protein, electrolytes, vitamins, and trace elements. They are hypertonic solutions. Most of the volume of TPN solutions is made up of macronutrients: amino acid solution (a source of protein) and a dextrose solution (a source of carbohydrate calories). Several electrolytes, trace elements, and multiple vitamins (together referred to as micronutrients) may be added to the base solution to meet individual patient requirements. Common electrolyte additives include sodium chloride (or acetate), potassium chloride (or acetate), calcium gluconate, magnesium sulfate, and sodium (or potassium) phosphate. Multiple vitamin preparations containing both water-soluble and fat-soluble vitamins are usually added on a daily basis. A trace element product containing zinc, copper, manganese, selenium, and chromium may be added.

IV fat emulsions

Intravenous fat (lipid) emulsion is required as a source of essential fatty acids. It is also used as a concentrated source of calories. Fat provides nine calories per gram, compared to 3.4 calories per gram provided by dextrose. Intravenous fat emulsion may be admixed into the parenteral nutrition solution with amino acids and dextrose, or piggybacked into the administration line.

peritoneal dialysis solutions

Used by patients who do not have functioning kidneys to remove toxic substances, excess body waste, and serum electrolytes through osmosis. The solution is administered directly into the peritoneal cavity (the cavity between the abdominal lining and the internal organs) to remove toxic substances, excess body waste, and serum electrolytes through osmosis. These solutions are hypertonic to blood so the water will not move into the circulatory system.

laminar flow hood

Establishes and maintains an ultraclean work area for the preparation of IV admixtures.

biological safety cabinets

Used in the preparation of hazardous drugs. They protect both personnel and the environment from contamination.

aseptic techniques

Maintain the sterility of all sterile items and are used in preparing IV admixtures.

syringes

Syringes come in sizes ranging from 1 to 60 ml. As a rule, a syringe size is used that is one size larger than the volume to be measured. The volume of solution in a syringe is measured to the edge of the plunger's stopper while the syringe is held upright and all air has been removed from the syringe.

needle sizes

Needle sizes are indicated by length and gauge. The higher the gauge number, the smaller is the lumen (the hollow bore of the needle shaft). Large needles may be needed with highly viscous solutions but are more likely to cause coring.

filters

Often used to remove contaminating particles from solutions. Depth filters and membrane filters are the two basic groups.

flow rate

The rate at which the solution is administered to the patient.

piggybacks

Small volumes of fluid (usually 50–100 ml) infused into the administration set of an LVP solution.

pumps

Infusion pumps, syringe pumps, and ambulatory pumps are devices used to administer LVP solutions and control flow rates. Administration sets are threaded through infusion pumps, and the pumps control the gravity flow. Infusion pumps have made the infusion process much more accurate and easier to administer and have been a major factor in the growth of home infusion.

LAMINAR FLOW HOODS AND BIOLOGICAL SAFETY CABINETS

HEPA filter

intake filter

LAMINAR FLOW HOOD

With a Laminar flow hood, room air is drawn into a horizontal hood and passed through a prefilter to remove relatively large contaminants such as dust and lint. The air is then channeled through a high efficiency particulate air (HEPA) filter that removes particles larger than 0.3 μm (microns). The purified air then flows over the work surface in parallel lines at a uniform velocity (i.e., laminar flow). The constant flow of air from the hood prevents room air from entering the work area and removes contaminants introduced into the work area by material or personnel.

top down view

HEPA filter

BIOLOGICAL SAFETY CABINETS

Biological safety cabinets protect both personnel and the environment from contamination. They are used in the preparation of hazardous drugs. A biological safety cabinet functions by passing air through a HEPA filter and directing it down toward the work area. As the air approaches the work surface, it is pulled through vents at the front, back, and sides of the hood. A major portion of the air is recirculated back into the cabinet and a minor portion passes through a secondary HEPA filter and is exhausted into the room.

RULES FOR WORKING WITH FLOW AND SAFETY HOODS

✔ **Never sneeze, cough, talk directly into a hood.**

✔ **Close doors or windows.** Breezes can disrupt the air flow sufficiently to contaminate the work area.

✔ **Perform all work at least 6 inches inside the hood** to derive the benefits of the laminar air flow. Laminar flow air begins to mix with outside air near the edge of the hood.

✔ **Maintain a direct, open path between the filter and the area inside the hood.**

✔ **Place nonsterile objects, such as solution containers or your hands, downstream from sterile ones.** Particles blown off these objects can contaminate anything downstream from them.

✔ **Do not put large objects at the back of the work area next to the filter.** They will disrupt air flow.

ASEPTIC TECHNIQUE

HAND WASHING

✔ Remove all jewelry and scrub hands and arms to the elbows with a suitable antibacterial agent.

✔ Stand far enough away from the sink so clothing does not come in contact with it.

✔ Turn on water. Wet hands and forearms thoroughly. Keep hands pointed downward.

✔ Scrub hands vigorously with an antibacterial soap.

✔ Work soap under fingernails by rubbing them against the palm of the other hand.

✔ Interlace the fingers and scrub the spaces between the fingers.

✔ Wash wrists and arms up to the elbows.

✔ Thoroughly rinse the soap from hands and arms.

✔ Dry hands and forearms thoroughly using a nonshedding paper towel.

✔ Use a dry paper towel to turn off the water faucet.

✔ After hands are washed, avoid touching clothes, face, hair, or any other potentially contaminated object in the area.

CLOTHING AND BARRIERS

✔ Wear clean lint-free garments or barrier clothing, including gowns, hair covers, and a mask.

✔ Wear sterile gloves.

✔ Follow facility or manufacturer guidelines for putting on and removing barrier clothing. Unless barriers are put on properly, they can easily become contaminated.

TRUE/FALSE

Indicate whether the statement is true or false in the blank. Answers are at the end of the book.

_____ 1.   Pyrogens are a micronutrient in parenteral solutions.

_____ 2.   0.9% sodium chloride is an isotonic solution.

_____ 3.   Physiological pH is about 7.4.

_____ 4.   Coring is more likely to occur with a 27 gauge needle than a 13 gauge needle.

_____ 5.   Class 2 Type A Biological Safety Cabinets provide the minimum recommended environment for preparing chemotherapy agents.

_____ 6.   5% dextrose is used as an irrigation solution.

EXPLAIN WHY

Explain why these statements are true or important. Check your answers in the text. Discuss any questions you may have with your Instructor.

1.   Why should intravenous solutions generally be isotonic?

2.   Why is the position of objects on a laminar flow hood work surface important?

3.   Why is visual inspection of parenteral solutions important?

IN THE WORKPLACE

Use these tools to practice and check some of your workplace skills.

Name: _____

Pharmacy Technician Skills Checklist
ASEPTIC TECHNIQUE: HAND WASHING

Skill or Procedure	Self-Assessment		Supervisor Review		
	Needs to Improve	Meets or Exceeds	Needs to Improve*	Meets or Exceeds	*Plan of Action
1. Removes all jewelry and scrubs hands and arms to the elbows with suitable antibacterial agent.					
2. Stands far enough away from sink so clothing does not come in contact with sink.					
3. Turns on water, wets hands and forearms thoroughly, keeps hands pointed downward.					
4. Scrubs hands vigorously with antibacterial soap.					
5. Works soap under fingernails by rubbing them against the palm of the other hand.					
6. Interlaces fingers and scrubs the spaces between the fingers.					
7. Washes wrists and arms up to the elbows.					
8. Thoroughly rinses the soap from hands and arms.					
9. Dries hands and forearms thoroughly using a nonshedding paper towel.					
10. Uses a dry paper towel to turn off water faucet.					

Name: _____

Pharmacy Technician Skills Checklist
LAMINAR FLOW HOOD

Skill or Procedure	Self-Assessment		Supervisor Review		
	Needs to Improve	Meets or Exceeds	Needs to Improve*	Meets or Exceeds	*Plan of Action
1. Turns on and lets run for at least 30 minutes prior to use.					
2. Does not allow jewelry, long sleeves, or other non-sterile materials within the hood.					
3. Uses clean gauze/sponge to clean hood with 70% isopropyl alcohol.					
4. Uses long side-to-side motions on the back surface of the hood and works from top to bottom to clean hood.					
5. Uses back-to-front motions, working from the top to the bottom of each side to clean the sides of the hood.					
6. Uses back-to-front motions to clean the surface of the hood.					
7. Takes care so that cleaned surfaces do not become contaminated during cleaning.					
8. Takes care when placing items in hood so that airflow is not blocked.					
9. Takes care when preparing admixtures, that airflow is not blocked by hands or other objects.					
10. Takes care so that hands remain under the hood during admixture preparation, and does not leave the hood during admixture preparation.					
11. Does not utilize outer 6 inches of hood opening or work too closely to sides and back of hood during drug preparation and manipulations.					
12. Does not contaminate hood by coughing, sneezing, chewing gum, or excessive talking.					

IN THE WORKPLACE

Use these tools to practice and check some of your workplace skills.

Name: _____

Pharmacy Technician Skills Checklist
GLASS AMPULES

Skill or Procedure	Self-Assessment		Supervisor Review		
	Needs to Improve	Meets or Exceeds	Needs to Improve*	Meets or Exceeds	*Plan of Action
1. If ampule is not pre-scored, uses a fine file to lightly score the neck of the ampule at its narrowest point.					
2. Holds ampule upright and taps the top.					
3. Swabs neck of ampule with an alcohol swab.					
4. Wraps gauze pad around neck of ampule and quickly snaps ampule moving hands outward and away.					
5. Inspects opened ampule for glass particles.					
6. Tilts ampule (about 20 degree angle).					
7. Inserts needle into ampule, so needle point does not touch opening of ampule.					
8. Positions needle into solution placing beveled edge against side of ampule.					
9. Withdraws correct amount of the drug while keeping the needle submerged.					
10. Withdraws needle from ampule and removes air bubbles from syringe					
11. Transfers solution to final container using filter needle or membrane filter.					

Name: _____

Pharmacy Technician Skills Checklist
VIAL WITH SOLUTION

Skill or Procedure	Self-Assessment		Supervisor Review		
	Needs to Improve	Meets or Exceeds	Needs to Improve*	Meets or Exceeds	*Plan of Action
1. Takes care in removing vial cover.					
2. Uses care in cleaning top of vial with alcohol wipe.					
3. Draws into syringe a volume of air equal to the volume of drug to be withdrawn.					
4. Penetrates the vial without coring and injects air.					
5. Turns the vial upside down and withdraws correct amount of drug into syringe.					
6. Withdraws needle from vial and with needle end up, taps syringe to allow air bubbles to come to the top of the syringe. Presses plunger to remove air and excess solution.					
7. Transfers solution into the IV bag or bottle, minimizing coring.					

IN THE WORKPLACE

Use these tools to practice and check some of your workplace skills.

Pharmacy Technician Skills Checklist
VIAL WITH POWDER

Name: _____

Skill or Procedure	Self-Assessment		Supervisor Review		
	Needs to Improve	Meets or Exceeds	Needs to Improve*	Meets or Exceeds	*Plan of Action
1. Takes care in removing vial cover.					
2. Uses care in cleaning top of vial with alcohol wipe.					
3. Draws into syringe a volume of air equal to the volume of diluent to be withdrawn.					
4. Penetrates the diluent vial without coring and injects air.					
5. Turns the diluent vial upside down and withdraws correct amount of diluent into syringe.					
6. Injects diluent into medication vial, and then withdraws a slight amount of air.					
7. Shakes vial until drug dissolves (unless shaking is not recommended)					
8. Reinserts needle and removes proper volume of drug solution (without injecting air).					
9. Removes all bubbles from syringe and transfers reconstituted solution to final container.					

Name: _____

Pharmacy Technician Skills Checklist
ADDING A DRUG (SVP) TO AN LVP

Skill or Procedure	Self-Assessment		Supervisor Review		
	Needs to Improve	Meets or Exceeds	Needs to Improve*	Meets or Exceeds	*Plan of Action
1. Removes protective covering from LVP package.					
2. Assembles the needle and syringe.					
3. If drug is in powder form, reconstitutes drug with recommended diluent.					
4. Swabs the SVP with an alcohol swab and draws the necessary volume of drug solution.					
5. Swabs the medication port of the LVP with an alcohol swab.					
6. Inserts needle into the medication port and through the inner diaphragm (medication port is fully extended).					
7. Injects the SVP solution.					
8. Removes the needle.					
9. Shakes and inspects the admixture					

FILL IN THE KEY TERM

Answers are at the end of the book.

additive	depth filter	hypertonic	piggybacks
admixture	dialysis	hypotonic	pyrogens
ampules	diluent	irrigation solution	RCRA
aseptic techniques	final filter	isotonic	ready-to-mix systems
bevel	Flashball	laminar flow	sharps
biological safety	flow rate	lumen	SVP solution
cabinets	gauge	LVP solution	TNA solution
chemical complexation	HEPA filter	lyophilized	TPN solution
coring	heparin lock	membrane filter	valence

1. _____ : Techniques that maintain sterile condition.

2. _____ : Chemicals produced by microorganisms that can cause pyretic (fever) reactions in patients.

3. _____ : Flexible rubber tubing at the end of a needle on an administration set.

4. _____ : When a solution has an osmolarity equivalent to another.

5. _____ : When a solution has a greater osmolarity than another.

6. _____ : When a solution has a lesser osmolarity than another.

7. _____ : The rate (in ml/hour or ml/minute) at which the solution is administered to the patient.

8. _____ : An injection device which uses heparin to keep blood from clotting in the device.

9. _____ : Small volume solutions added to an LVP.

10. _____ : When two drugs combine and form a new chemical.

11. _____ : The resulting solution when a drug is added to a parenteral solution.

12. _____ : Freeze-dried.

13. _____ : A liquid that dilutes a substance or solution.

14. _____ : Systems with predetermined amounts of admixture components for which admixing takes place just prior to administration.

15. _____ : An angled surface, as with the tip of a needle.

16. _____ : With needles, the higher the number, the thinner the lumen.

17. _____ : The hollow center of a needle.

18. _____ : When a needle damages the rubber closure of a parenteral container, causing fragments of the closure to fall into the container and contaminate its contents.

19. _____ : A filter that attaches to a syringe and filters solution through a membrane as the solution is expelled from the syringe.

20. _____ : A filter placed inside a needle hub that can filter solutions being drawn in or expelled, but not both.

21. _____ : A filter that filters solution immediately before it enters a patient's vein.

22. _____ : Continuous movement at a stable rate in one direction.

23. _____ : A high efficiency particulate air filter.

24. _____ : Are used in the preparation of hazardous drugs and protect both personnel and the environment from contamination.

25. _____ : Large splash solutions used during surgical or urologic procedures to bathe and moisten body tissue.

26. _____ : Sealed glass containers with an elongated neck that must be snapped off.

27. _____ : Needles, jagged glass or metal objects, or any items that might puncture or cut the skin.

28. _____ : A drug that is added to a parenteral solution.

29. _____ : Regulates handling hazardous waste.

30. _____ : The number of positive or negative charges on an ion.

31. _____ : Commonly 100, 250, 500, and 1,000 mL IV solution.

32. _____ : Packaged product either directly administered to a patient or added to another parenteral.

33. _____ : Intravenous solution with amino acids, dextrose, and additional micronutrients.

34. _____ : Intravenous solution with amino acids, dextrose, fat emulsion, and additional micronutrients.

35. _____ : Movement of particles in a solution through permeable membranes.

CHOOSE THE BEST ANSWER

Answers are at the end of the book.

1. Pyrogens are chemicals that are produced by
   a. coring.
   b. microorganisms.
   c. precipitation.
   d. heat.

2. A(an) _____ solution has greater osmolarity than blood.
   a. hypotonic
   b. isotonic
   c. hypertonic
   d. pyrogenic

3. Piggybacks usually contain _____ of fluid and are infused over a period of 30-60 minutes.
   a. 50–100 ml
   b. 250–500 ml
   c. 5000–1000 ml
   d. 1000 ml–2000 ml

4. When a drug is added to a parenteral solution, the drug is referred to as the _____ and the final mixture is referred to as the _____.
   a. admixture, additive
   b. suspension, solution
   c. additive, admixture
   d. solution, suspension

5. Some examples of ready-to-mix systems include
   a. heparin lock and Ringer's solution.
   b. Luer-Lok® and Slip-Lok®.
   c. Add-Vantage®, Add-a-Vial®, and Mini-Bag Plus®.
   d. Ringer's solution and Lactated Ringer's solution.

6. _____ is the part of the needle that attaches to the syringe.
   a. The lumen
   b. The bevel
   c. The coring
   d. The hub

7. _____ are filters that can be placed inside of needles.
   a. Membrane filters
   b. Filter needles
   c. HEPA filters
   d. Intake filters

8. In horizontal laminar flow hoods, air blows
   a. down toward the work area.
   b. away from the operator.
   c. toward the operator.
   d. up toward the HEPA filter.

9. Biological Safety Cabinets have
   a. vertical air flow down toward the work.
   b. horizontal air flow away from the operator.
   c. vertical air flow up toward the HEPA filter.
   d. horizontal air flow toward the operator.

10. When positioning supplies for use in a laminar flow hood
    a. larger supplies should be placed closer to the HEPA filter.
    b. smaller supplies should be placed closer to the HEPA filter.
    c. space the supplies close together to minimize laminar flow.
    d. the spacing of supplies has no effect on laminar flow.

11. Sharps containers should be disposed of when _____ full.
    a. 1/3
    b. 1/2
    c. 2/3
    d. 3/4

12. If an ampule has not been pre-scored, the technician should
    a. score the neck of the ampule with a fine file.
    b. use sterile pliers to open the ampule.
    c. use a file to file all the way through the neck.
    d. just snap the ampule since manufacturers always pre-score when necessary.

13. If 500 mg of a drug are added to a 100 mL IV bag, what is the percent strength of the resulting solution?
    a. 0.0005%
    b. 0.005%
    c. 0.05%
    d. 0.5%

14. What is the molecular weight of $CaCl_2$ if the atomic weight of Ca is 40.08 and the atomic weight of Cl is 35.43?
    a. 70.86
    b. 110.94
    c. 75.51
    d. 106.29

15. What is the valence of NaCl?
    a. 0
    b. 2
    c. 1

16. What is the weight of one osmole of NaCl? (molecular weight = 58.4)
    a. 58.4 g
    b. 58.4 mg
    c. 29.2 g
    d. 29.2 mg

STUDY NOTES

Use this area to write important points you'd like to remember.

— 9 —

COMPOUNDING

KEY CONCEPTS

Test your knowledge by covering the information in the right hand column.

extemporaneous compounding	The on-demand preparation of a drug product according to a physician's prescription, formula, or recipe.
accuracy and stability	The supervising pharmacist must determine that a product can be accurately compounded and will be stable for its expected use. Accuracy is then essential in all weighings, measurements, and other activities in the compounding process.
class A balances	Can weigh as little as 120 mg of material with a 5% error. Always use the balance on a level surface and in a draft-free area. Always arrest the balance before adding or removing weight from either pan, or storing.
sensitivity	The amount of weight that will move the balance pointer one division mark.
electronic or analytical balances	Highly sensitive balances that can weigh quantities smaller than 120 mg with acceptable accuracy.
weighing papers or boats	Should always be placed on the balance pans before any weighing is done. Balances must be readjusted after a new weighing paper or boat has been placed on each pan. Weighing papers taken from the same box can vary in weight by as much as 65 mg.
mortar and pestle	Made of three types of materials: glass, wedgewood; and porcelain. Wedgewood and porcelain mortars are used to grind crystals and large particles into fine powders. Glass mortars and pestles are preferable for mixing liquids and semi solid dosage forms.
volumetric glassware	For weighing liquid drugs, solvents, or additives. Includes graduates, flasks, pipets, and syringes. Erlenmeyer flasks, beakers, and prescription bottles, regardless of markings, are not volumetric glassware.

small volumes	Always use the smallest device (graduate, pipet, syringe) that will accommodate the desired volume of liquid.
graduated cylinders	Cylindrical graduates are preferred over cone shaped because they are more accurate. When selecting a graduate, always choose the smallest graduate capable of containing the volume to be measured. Avoid measurements of volumes that are below 20 percent of the capacity of the graduate because the accuracy is unacceptable.
disposable syringe	Used to measure small volumes. Measurements made with syringes are more accurate and precise than those made with cylindrical graduates. Measure volumes to the edge of the syringe stopper.
meniscus	The curved surface of a volume of liquid. When reading a volume of a liquid against a graduation mark, hold the graduate so the meniscus is at eye level and read the mark at the bottom of the meniscus.
medicine droppers	Used to deliver small liquid doses, but must first be calibrated.
trituration	The fine grinding of a powder.
levigation	The trituration of a powdered drug with a solvent in which the drug is insoluble to reduce the particle size of the drug.
geometric dilution	A technique for mixing two powders of unequal size. The smaller amount of powder is diluted in steps by additions of the larger amount of powder.
solvents	Water is the most common solvent, but ethanol, glycerin, propylene glycol, or a variety of syrups may be used.
syrup	A concentrated or nearly saturated solution of sucrose in water. Syrups containing flavoring agents are known as flavoring syrups (e.g. cherry syrup, acacia syrup, etc.).
nonaqueous solutions	Solutions that contain solvents other than water.
thickening agents	Reduce the settling (sedimentation rate) of a suspension.
suspensions	A "two-phase" compound consisting of a finely divided solid dispersed in a liquid. Most solid drugs are levigated in a mortar to reduce the particle size as much as possible before adding to the vehicle. Common levigating agents are alcohol or glycerin.
flocculating agents	Electrolytes that carry an electrical charge and enhance particle "dispersibility" in a solution.
ointments and creams	Ointments are simple mixtures of a drug(s) in an ointment base. A cream is a semi-solid emulsion. Oleaginous (oil based) bases generally release substances slowly and unpredictably. Water miscible or aqueous bases tend to release drugs more rapidly.

KEY CONCEPTS

Test your knowledge by covering the information in the right hand column.

emulsion	An unstable system consisting of at least two immiscible (unmixable) liquids, one that is dispersed as small droplets throughout the other, and a stabilizing agent.
oil-in-water (o/w)	An emulsion of oils, petroleum hydrocarbons, and/or waxes with water, where the aqueous phase is generally in excess of 45% of the total weight of the emulsion.
water-in-oil (w/o)	When water or aqueous solutions are dispersed in an oleaginous (oil based) medium, with the aqueous phase constituting less than 45% of the total weight.
emulsifiers	Emulsifiers provide a protective barrier around the dispersed droplets that stabilize the emulsion. Commonly used emulsifiers include: tragacanth, sodium lauryl sulfate, sodium dioctyl sulfosuccinate, and polymers known as the Spans® and Tweens®.
suppository bases	There are three classes that are based on their composition and physical properties: oleaginous bases, water soluble or miscible bases, and hydrophilic bases.
polyethylene glycols (PEGs)	Popular water soluble bases that are chemically stable, non-irritating, miscible with water and mucous secretions, and can be formulated by molding or compression in a wide range of hardnesses and melting points.
fusion molding	A method in which the drug is dispersed or dissolved in a melted suppository base. The fusion method can be used with all types of suppositories and must be used with most of them.
compression molding	A method of preparing suppositories by mixing the suppository base and the drug ingredients and forcing the mixture into a special compression mold.
capsules	When filling, the smallest capsule capable of containing the final volume is used since patients often have difficulty swallowing large capsules.

USING A BALANCE

Class A Balance

weights　　leveling feet　arrest knob

BASIC GUIDELINES FOR USING BALANCES

There are some general rules about using a balance that help to maintain the balance in top condition.

✔ Always cover both pans with weighing papers or use weighing boats. These protect the pans from abrasions, eliminate the need for repeated washing, and reduce loss of drug to porous surfaces.

✔ A clean paper or boat should be used for each new ingredient to prevent contamination of components.

✔ The balance must be readjusted after a new weighing paper or boat has been placed on each pan. Weighing papers taken from the same box can vary in weight by as much as 65 mg. If the new zero point is not established, an error of as much as 65 mg can be made. On 200 mg of material, this is more than 30%. Weighing boats also vary in weight.

✔ Always arrest the balance before adding or removing weight from either pan. Although the balance is noted for its durability, repeated jarring of the balance will ultimately damage the working mechanism of the balance and reduce its accuracy.

✔ Always clean the balance, close the lid, and arrest the pans before storing the balance between uses.

✔ Always use the balance on a level surface and in a draft-free area.

MEASURING

MENISCUS

When reading a volume of a liquid against a graduation mark, hold the graduate so the meniscus is at eye level and read the mark at the bottom of the meniscus. Viewing the level from above will create the incorrect impression that there is more volume in the graduate. If the container is very narrow, the meniscus can be quite large.

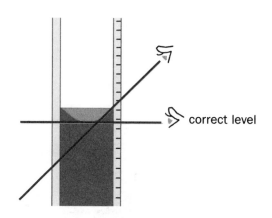

correct level

SYRINGE

When reading a volume of a liquid in a syringe, read to the edge of the stopper.

correct volume

CAPSULE SIZES

The relative sizes and fill capacities of capsules are:

Size	Volume (ml)
000	1.37
00	0.95
0	0.68
1	0.5
2	0.37
3	0.3
4	0.2
5	0.13

the punch method
of filling capsules

TRUE/FALSE

Indicate whether the statement is true or false in the blank. Answers are at the end of the book.

_____ 1.   Compounding must always be done upon receipt of a prescription, never in advance.

_____ 2.   Quantities smaller than 120 mg should be weighed on an electronic or analytical balance.

_____ 3.   Cylindrical graduates are more accurate than conical ones.

_____ 4.   Mineral oil is a common levigating agent.

_____ 5.   Disposable syringes are generally used for measuring small volumes.

_____ 6.   When aqueous and non-aqueous solutions are mixed, the volume is always equal to the sum of the two volumes.

_____ 7.   The punch method is a method to prepare suppositories.

_____ 8.   Syrup USP is a supersaturated solution.

_____ 9.   Flocculating agents are used to reduce the sedimentation rate in suspensions.

_____ 10.   PEGs with molecular weight over 1,000 are solids.

_____ 11.   An emulsion containing 48% water would be a water-in-oil emulsion.

_____ 12.   Capsule size 000 can hold more ingredient than capsule size 5.

EXPLAIN WHY

Explain why these statements are true or important. Check your answers in the text. Discuss any questions you may have with your Instructor.

1.   Why is the stability of a compound important?

2.   Why is accuracy in each step of compounding important?

3.   Why is the smallest device that will accommodate a volume used to measure it?

4.   Why are class A balances not used for very small amounts?

5.   Why is geometric dilution used when mixing unequal amounts of powders?

IN THE WORKPLACE

Sample Formulation Record

Formulation Record

Name: _____

Strength: _____

Dosage Form: _____

Route of Administration: _____

Date of Last Review or Revision: _____

Person Completing Last Review or Revision: _____

Formula: [*The formula and all of the information about the individual ingredients are described.*]

Ingredient	Quantity	Physical Description	Solubility	Therapeutic Activity

Example Calculations: [*Examples of calculations that must be made each time the formula is compounded are shown.*]

Equipment Required:

Method of Preparation:

1. [*The method is a step-by-step sequence in the correct order of mixing.*]

2. [*The description of should be clear and detailed so all personnel can complete the step in exactly the same manner.*]

3. [*The description can also consist of graphs, tables, charts, etc.*]

Description of Finished Product:

Formulation Record - Page 2

Name: _____

Strength: _____

Dosage Form: _____

Route of Administration: _____

Quality Control Procedures: [*Details of all quality assurance tests to be performed on final product.*]

Packaging Container:

Storage Requirements:

Beyond-Use Date Assignment: [*Criteria used to assign a beyond-use date.*]

Label Information: [*Auxiliary labels to include.*]

Source of Recipe:

Literature Information: [*Copies of relevant references or primary literature.*]

IN THE WORKPLACE

Sample Compounding Record

Compounding Record

Name: _____

Strength: _____

Dosage Form: _____

Route of Administration: _____

Quantity Prepared: _____

Date of Preparation: _____

Person Preparing Formulation: _____

Person Checking Formulation: _____

Formula: [*This information is completed at the time of compounding.*]

Ingredient	Manufacturer and Lot Number	Purity Grade	Description	Quantity Required	Actual Quantity Used

Calculations: [Calculations performed at the time of compounding.]

Equipment Operation: [*Equipment performance notes or alternate equipment used.*]

Method of Preparation: [*Description of any deviation from the Formulation Record method of preparation.*]

Description of Finished Product:

Quality Control Procedures: [*Details of quality assurance test results and data.*]

Beyond-Use Date Assignment: [*Assigned beyond-use date and reasons for difference from Formulation Record if applicable.*]

In the Workplace

Sample Standard Operating Procedure Form

<table>
<tr><td colspan="5" align="center">**Standard Operating Procedure**</td></tr>
<tr><td rowspan="4">Subject:

[*What the SOP is concerning*]</td><td colspan="4" align="center">Policies and Procedures</td></tr>
<tr><td>Effective Date:</td><td>Revision Date</td><td colspan="2">Revision No.</td></tr>
<tr><td>Approved by:</td><td>Reviewed by:</td><td></td></tr>
<tr><td>[*Additional Items*]</td><td>[*Additional Items*]</td><td colspan="2">[*Additional Items*]</td></tr>
</table>

Purpose of the SOP: [*Describe the purpose and the desired outcome of the SOP.*]

Procedure:

1.   [*The procedure is a step-by-step sequence in the order of tasks to perform.*]

2.   [*The description of should be clear and detailed so all personnel can complete the step in exactly the same manner*].

3.   [*The description can also consist of graphs, tables, charts, etc.*]

Documentation:

   [*Executing the SOP may generate data or information that needs to be documented. This information may be best reported on a form and maintained in a separate notebook or binder. The form should refer to the execution of the SOP by including the name of the procedure, date it was executed, personnel name conducting the procedure, and then the relevant data or information.*]

FILL IN THE KEY TERM

Answers are at the end of the book.

aliquot	formulation record	primary emulsion	USP/NF Chapter
arrest knob	fusion molding	primary standard	<795>
calibrate	geometric dilution	punch method	USP/NF Chapter
compression molding	hydrophilic emulsifier	sensitivity	<797>
emulsifier	levigation	sonication	USP/NF grade
emulsion	lipophilic emulsifier	spatulation	volumetric
extemporaneous	meniscus	syrup	water-in-oil
compounding	mucilage	thickening agent	
flocculating agent	oil-in-water	trituration	

1. _____ : The on-demand preparation of a drug product according to a physician's prescription, formula, or recipe.

2. _____ : Regulations pertaining to nonsterile compounding or formulations.

3. _____ : Regulations that pertain to sterile compounding or formulations.

4. _____ : To set, mark, or check the graduations of a measuring device.

5. _____ : Measures volume.

6. _____ : The knob on a balance that prevents any movement of the balance.

7. _____ : The curved surface of a column of liquid.

8. _____ : The fine grinding of a powder.

9. _____ : Triturating a powdered drug with a solvent in which it is insoluble to reduce its particle size.

10. _____ : A technique for mixing two powders of unequal size.

11. _____ : Exposure to high frequency sound waves.

12. _____ : Mixing powders with a spatula.

13. _____ : Formulas and procedures of what should happen when a formulation is compounded.

14. _____ : A portion of a mixture.

15. _____ : A concentrated or nearly saturated solution of sucrose in water.

16. _____ : The amount of weight that will move the balance pointer one division mark.

17. _____ : Electrolytes used in the preparation of suspensions.

18. _____ : An agent used in the preparation of suspensions to increase the viscosity of the liquid.

19. _____ : Lowest grade of purity for an ingredient in a compound.

20. _____ : The highest grade of purity for an ingredient.

21. _____ : A stabilizing agent in emulsions.

22. _____ : An unstable system consisting of at least two immiscible liquids.

23. _____ : An emulsion in which water is dispersed through an oil base.

24. _____ : An emulsion in which oil is dispersed through a water base.

25. _____ : A stabilizing agent for water based dispersion mediums.

26. _____ : A stabilizing agent for oil based dispersion mediums.

27. _____ : The initial emulsion formed in a preparation to which ingredients are added to create the final volume.

28. _____ : A wet, slimy preparation formed as an initial step in a wet emulsion preparation method.

29. _____ : A method of making suppositories in which the ingredients are compressed in a mold.

30. _____ : A suppository preparation method in which the active ingredients are dispersed in a melted suppository base.

31. _____ : A method for filling capsules by repeatedly pushing or "punching" the capsule into an amount of drug powder.

STUDY NOTES

Use this area to write important points you'd like to remember.

CHOOSE THE BEST ANSWER

Answers are at the end of the book.

1. The _____ has the federal authority to set standards pertaining to pharmacy compounding.
   a. USP
   b. FDA
   c. ASHP
   d. DEA

2. The storage temperature definition for a refrigerator is
   a. -20°C to -10°C.
   b. 2°C–8°C.
   c. 8°C–15°C.
   d. 30°C–40°C.

3. The minimum weighable quantity for a class A balance is
   a. 120 mg.
   b. 500 ml.
   c. 120 ml.
   d. 500 mg.

4. Metric weights used for weighing ingredients using a class A balance should be handled with
   a. water.
   b. fingers.
   c. forceps.
   d. oil.

5. Quantities less than 120 mg
   a. may be measured using a class A balance.
   b. may be measured using electronic or analytical balances.
   c. may be measured using a class C balance.
   d. may be measured using a class B balance.

6. _____ is the term for triturating a powdered drug with a solvent in which it is insoluble to reduce its particle size.
   a. Suspension
   b. Trituration
   c. Emulsion
   d. Levigation

7. Mixing powders using a spatula is called
   a. extemporaneous compounding.
   b. spatulation.
   c. emulsification.
   d. levigation.

8. A solution that contains the maximum amount of drug it can contain at room temperature is
   a. supersaturated.
   b. saturated.
   c. unsaturated.
   d. eutectic.

9. An appropriate flavoring for a bitter tasting drug is
   a. cherry.
   b. orange.
   c. cinnamon.
   d. anise.

10. _____ are electrolytes used in the preparation of suspensions.
    a. Flocculating agents
    b. Suspending agents
    c. Complex carbohydrates
    d. Simple sugars

11. A two-phase system consisting of a finely divided solid dispersed in a liquid is a/an
    a. suspension.
    b. emulsion.
    c. solution.
    d. trituration.

12. _____ are thickening agents used in the preparation of suspensions.
    a. Electrolytes
    b. Preservatives
    c. Flocculating agents
    d. Suspending agents

13. An example of an oleaginous base is
    a. Fattibase®.
    b. glycerinated gelatin.
    c. PEG 1540.
    d. glycerin.

14. The method of choice for making emulsions with the consistency of a lotion or cream is the
    a. continental method.
    b. beaker method.
    c. wet gum method.
    d. dry gum method.

15. Polyethylene glycol (PEG) polymers are used to make _____ suppositories.
    a. cocoa butter
    b. water soluble or miscible
    c. oleaginous
    d. hydrophilic

16. _____ are mixtures of oleaginous and water miscible bases for making suppositories.
    a. Hydrophobic bases
    b. Hydrophonic
    c. Hydrophilic bases
    d. Hydrotonic bases

STUDY NOTES

Use this area to write important points you'd like to remember.

— 10 —

BASIC BIOPHARMACEUTICS

KEY CONCEPTS

Test your knowledge by covering the information in the right hand column.

objective of drug therapy	To deliver the right drug, in the right concentration, to the right site of action at the right time to produce the desired effect.
receptors	When a drug produces an effect, it is interacting on a molecular level with cell material that is called a receptor. Receptor activation is responsible for most of the pharmacological responses in the body.
site of action	Only those drugs able to interact with the receptors in a particular site of action can produce effects in that site. This is why specific cells only respond to certain drugs.
agonists	Drugs that activate receptors and produce a response that may either accelerate or slow normal cell processes.
antagonists	Drugs that bind to receptors but do not activate them. They prevent other drugs or substances from interacting with receptors.
dose-response curve	Specific doses of a drug is given to various subjects and the effect or response is measured in terms of dose and effect.
blood concentration	The primary way to monitor a drug's concentration in the body and its related effect is to determine its blood concentrations.
minimum effective concentration (MEC)	When there is enough drug at the site of action to produce a response.
minimum toxic concentration (MTC)	An upper blood concentration limit beyond which there are undesired or toxic effects.
therapeutic window	The range between the minimum effective concentration and the minimum toxic concentration is called the therapeutic window. When concentrations are in this range, most

patients receive the maximum benefit from their drug therapy with a minimum of risk.

ADME

Blood concentrations are the result of four simultaneously acting processes: absorption, distribution, metabolism, and excretion.

half-life

The amount of time it takes for the blood concentration of a drug to decline to one-half of an initial value.

disposition

Another term for ADME.

elimination

Metabolism and excretion combined.

passive diffusion

Besides the four ADME processes, a critical factor of drug concentration and effect is how drugs move through biological membranes. Most drugs penetrate biological membranes by passive diffusion.

hydrophobic drugs

Lipid (fat) soluble drugs that penetrate the lipoidal (fat-like) cell membrane better than hydrophilic drugs.

hydrophilic drugs

Drugs that are attracted to water.

aqueous pores

Openings in cell membranes that allow entry of water and water soluble drugs.

absorption

The transfer of drug into the blood from an administered drug product is called absorption.

gastric emptying

Most drugs are given orally and absorbed into the blood from the small intestine. One of the primary factors affecting oral drug absorption is the gastric emptying time.

distribution

The movement of a drug within the body once the drug has reached the blood.

selective action

Drug action that is selective to certain tissues or organs, due both to the specific nature of receptor action as well as to various factors that can affect distribution.

protein binding

Many drugs bind to proteins in blood plasma to form a complex that is too large to penetrate cell openings. So the drug remains inactive.

metabolism

The body's process of transforming drugs. The primary site of drug metabolism in the body is the liver. Enzymes produced by the liver interact with drugs and transform them into metabolites.

enzyme	A complex protein that causes chemical reactions in other substances.
metabolite	The transformed drug.
enzyme induction	The increase in enzyme activity that results in greater metabolism of drugs.
enzyme inhibition	The decrease in enzyme activity that results in reduced metabolism of drugs.
first-pass metabolism	When a drug is substantially degraded or destroyed by the liver's enzymes before it reaches the circulatory system, an important factor with orally administered drugs.
enterohepatic cycling	The transfer of drugs and their metabolites from the liver to the bile in the gall bladder and then into the intestine.
excretion	The process of excreting drugs and metabolites, primarily performed by the kidney through the urine.
glomerular filtration	The blood filtering process of the kidneys. As plasma water moves through the nephron, waste substances (including drugs and metabolites) are secreted into the fluid, with urine as the end result.
bioavailability	The amount of a drug that is delivered to the site of action and the rate at which it is available is called the bioavailability of the drug.
bioequivalents	Bioequivalent drug products are pharmaceutical equivalents or alternatives which have essentially the same rate and extent of absorption when administered at the same dose of the active ingredient under similar conditions.
pharmaceutical equivalents	Pharmaceutical equivalents are drug products that contain identical amounts of the same active ingredients in the same dosage form, but may contain different inactive ingredients.
pharmaceutical alternatives	Pharmaceutical alternatives are drug products that contain the identical active ingredients, but not necessarily in the same amount or dosage form.
therapeutic equivalent	Pharmaceutical equivalents that produce the same effects in patients.
therapeutic alternative	Drugs that have different active ingredients but produce similar therapeutic effects.

DOSE RESPONSE CURVE

When a series of specific doses is given to a number of people, the results show that some people respond to low doses but others require larger doses for a response to be produced. Some differences are due to the product itself, but most are due to human variability: different people have different characteristics that affect how a drug product behaves in them. A dose-response curve shows that as doses increase, responses increase up to a point where increased dosage no longer results in increased response.

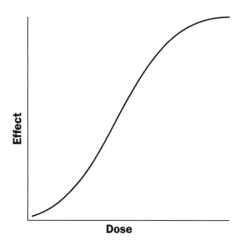

BLOOD CONCENTRATION—TIME PROFILES

Blood concentration begins at zero at the time the drug is administered (before it has been absorbed into the blood). With time, the drug leaves the formulation and enters the blood, causing concentrations to rise. Minimum effective concentration (MEC) is when there is enough drug at the site of action to produce a response. The time this occurs is called the onset of action. With most drugs, when blood concentrations increase, so does the intensity of the effect, since blood concentrations reflect the site of action concentrations that produce the response.

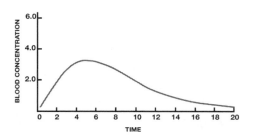

Some drugs have an upper blood concentration limit beyond which there are undesired or toxic effects. This limit is called the minimum toxic concentration (MTC). The range between the minimum effective concentration and the minimum toxic concentration is called the therapeutic window. When concentrations are in this range, most patients receive the maximum benefit from their drug therapy with a minimum of risk.

The last part of the curve shows the blood concentrations declining as absorption is complete. The time between the onset of action and the time when the minimum effective concentration is reached by the declining blood concentrations is called the duration of action. The duration of action is the time the drug should produce the desired effect.

ORAL ABSORPTION

Most drugs are given orally and absorbed into the blood from the small intestine. The small intestine's large surface area makes absorption easier. However, there are many conditions in the stomach that can affect absorption positively or negatively before the drug even reaches the small intestine. One of the primary factors affecting oral drug absorption is the gastric emptying time. This is the time a drug will stay in the stomach before it is emptied into the small intestine. Since stomach acid can degrade many drugs and since most absorption occurs in the intestine, gastric emptying time can significantly affect a drug's action. If a drug remains in the stomach too long, it can be degraded or destroyed, and its effect decreased. Gastric emptying time can be affected by a various conditions, including the amount and type of food in the stomach, the presence of other drugs, the person's body position, and their emotional condition. Some factors increase the gastric emptying time, but most slow it. The pH of the gastrointestinal organs is illustrated at right.

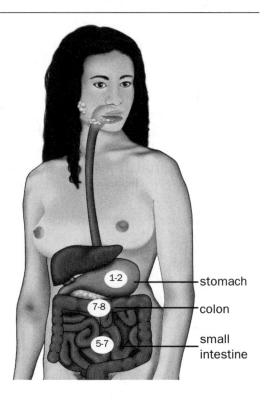

PASSIVE DIFFUSION

Before an effective concentration of a drug can reach its site of action, it must overcome many barriers, most of which are biological membranes, complex structures composed of lipids (fats) and proteins. Most drugs penetrate biological membranes by passive diffusion. This occurs when drugs in the body's fluids move from an area of higher concentration to an area of lower concentration, until the concentrations in each area are in a state of equilibrium. Passive diffusion causes most orally administered drugs to move from the intestine to the blood and from the blood to the site of action.

PROTEIN BINDING

Many drugs bind to proteins in blood plasma to form a complex that is too large to penetrate cell openings. So the drug remains inactive. Protein binding can be considered a type of drug storage within the body. Some drugs bind extensively to proteins in fat and muscle, and are gradually released as the blood concentration of the drug falls. These drugs remain in the body a long time, and therefore have a long duration of action.

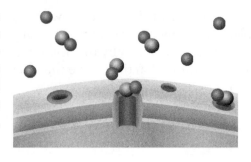

PHARMACOKINETICS (HALF-LIFE)

Besides providing correlations between a pharmacological effect and time, blood concentration-time profiles can be used to describe rate processes. The rate of transfer of an amount of drug from one location to another (e.g., drug transferred to the urine by urinary excretion) or from one chemical form to another (e.g., metabolism of active drug to inactive drug) are common examples of rate processes. Pharmacokinetics is the study of the ADME processes of the body that affect an administered drug.

The data from a blood concentration-time profile is used to determine the bioavailability and bioequivalency of drug products. The same data can be used to obtain three additional pharmacokinetic parameters: half-life of elimination, area-under-curve (AUC), and total body clearance.

HALF-LIFE OF ELIMINATION: This half-life is the amount of time it takes for a blood concentration to decline to one-half an initial value. For example, if at 6 hours, a blood concentration was 30 mcg/ml, and at 15 hours, the blood concentration was 15 mcg/ml, then the half-life would be equal to 9 hours (15 6 hours). For most cases, five times the half-life of elimination will estimate how long the elimination processes will be important in the disposition of the administered drug. In the example, 5 x 9 hours or 45 hours is low long it will take for the processes of elimination to essentially remove the drug from the body.

AREA-UNDER-CURVE: The AUC is a mathematical number expressing how much physical area is contained under the blood concentration-time profile. The units of AUC are concentration X time (mcg/ml x hours). The AUCs of formulations are used to help determine the bioequivalency of different dosage forms. It is also used to calculate another important pharmacokinetic parameter, total body clearance.

TOTAL BODY CLEARANCE: Total body clearance (Cl) reflects the combined effect of all processes eliminating the drug from the body: urinary excretion, metabolism, expiration through the lungs, and fecal excretion. The units of Cl are ml/min or ml/hour: clearance tells you the number of ml cleared of the drug per time unit. For example, if a drug's clearance is 120 ml/min, then 120 ml of volume is cleared of the drug every minute. That can be said from a conceptual point of view. But in the body, you don't just clear a portion of the volume. Distribution is an ongoing process, as is elimination, so any volume that is cleared will be "refilled" as soon as it is emptied. The overall effect is that blood concentrations continue to fall as the drug is cleared from the body.

FILL IN THE KEY TERM

Answers are at the end of the book.

active transport	enzyme induction	onset of action
agonist	enzyme inhibition	passive diffusion
antagonist	first pass metabolism	pharmaceutical alternative
bioavailability	gastric emptying time	pharmaceutical equivalent
bioequivalency	glomerular filtration	protein binding
biopharmaceutics	hydrophilic	receptor
complex	hydrophobic	selective action
disposition	lipoidal	site of action
enterohepatic cycling	metabolite	therapeutic equivalent
enzyme	minimum effective concentration	therapeutic window
	nephron	

1. _____ : The study of the factors associated with drug products and physiological processes, and the resulting systemic concentrations of the drugs.

2. _____ : The location where an administered drug produces an effect.

3. _____ : The cellular material at the site of action which interacts with the drug.

4. _____ : The characteristic of a drug that makes its action specific to certain receptors and the tissues they affect.

5. _____ : Drugs that activate receptors to accelerate or slow normal cell function.

6. _____ : Drugs that bind with receptors but do not activate them. They block receptor action by preventing other drugs or substances from activating them.

7. _____ : The blood concentration needed of a drug to produce a response.

8. _____ : The time MEC is reached and the response occurs.

9. _____ : A drug's blood concentration range between its minimum effective concentration and minimum toxic concentration.

10. _____ : A term sometimes used to refer to all of the ADME processes together.

11. _____ : The movement of drugs from an area of higher concentration to lower concentration.

12. _____ : The movement of drug molecules across membranes by active means, rather than passive diffusion.

13. _____ : Water repelling; cannot associate with water.

14. _____ : Capable of associating with or absorbing water.

15. _____ : Fat like substance.

16. _____ : The time a drug will stay in the stomach before it is emptied into the small intestine.

17. _____ : Formed when molecules of different chemicals attach to each other, as in protein binding.

18. _____ : The attachment of a drug molecule to a plasma or tissue protein, effectively making the drug inactive, but also keeping it within the body.

19. _____ : The substance resulting from the body's transformation of an administered drug.

20. _____ : A complex protein that causes chemical reactions in other substances.

21. _____ : The increase in enzyme activity that results in greater metabolism of drugs.

22. _____ : The decrease in enzyme activity that results in reduced metabolism of drugs.

23. _____ : The substantial degradation of a drug caused by enzyme metabolism in the liver before the drug reaches the systemic circulation.

24. _____ : The transfer of drugs and their metabolites from the liver to the bile in the gall bladder and then into the intestine.

25. _____ : The functional unit of the kidneys.

26. _____ : The blood filtering process of the kidneys.

27. _____ : The relative amount of an administered dose that reaches the general circulation and the rate at which this occurs.

28. _____ : The comparison of bioavailability between two dosage forms.

29. _____ : Drug products that contain identical amounts of the same active ingredients in the same dosage form.

30. _____ : Drug products that contain the same active ingredients, but not necessarily in the same amount or dosage form.

31. _____ : Pharmaceutical equivalents that produce the same effects in patients.

TRUE/FALSE

Indicate whether the statement is true or false in the blank. Answers are at the end of the book.

_____ 1. Receptors are located on the surfaces of cell membranes and inside cells.

_____ 2. Agonists may produce a response that slows normal cell process.

_____ 3. Antagonists bind to cell receptors but do not activate them.

_____ 4. After all receptors are occupied by a drug, its effect can still be increased by increasing the dose.

_____ 5. The number or sensitivity of receptors is not affected by prolonged drug use.

_____ 6. Most patients receive the maximum benefit from drug therapy when the amount of the drug in the blood is between the minimum effective and minimum toxic concentration.

_____ 7. Five times the half-life is used to estimate how long it takes for elimination from the body.

_____ 8. Cell membranes generally absorb hydrophilic drugs more easily than hydrophobic ones.

_____ 9. Most orally administered drugs are absorbed from the stomach.

_____ 10. Protein binding can result in the gradual release of a drug into the bloodstream.

_____ 11. Most drugs and metabolites are excreted by the liver.

EXPLAIN WHY

Explain why these statements are true or important. Check your answers in the text. Discuss any questions you may have with your Instructor.

1. Why can a drug be developed to have a specific therapeutic effect?

2. Why can the same drug have different effects in different people?

3. Why is gastric emptying time important?

4. Why does the chronic administration of some drugs require increases in dosage to achieve the same effect or decreases to avoid toxicity?

5. Why is a pharmaceutical equivalent not necessarily therapeutically equivalent?

CHOOSE THE BEST ANSWER

Answers are at the end of the book.

1. _____ are drugs that activate receptors to accelerate or slow normal cellular function.
    a. Channels
    b. Agonists
    c. Antagonists
    d. Protein binding

2. The time between the onset of action and the time when the MEC is reached by declining blood concentrations is the
    a. duration of action.
    b. MTC.
    c. therapeutic window.
    d. dose-response curve.

3. When studying concentration and effect, _____ is the time MEC is reached and the response occurs.
   a. therapeutic window
   b. MTC
   c. onset of action
   d. blood concentration

4. Most absorption of oral drugs occurs in the
   a. stomach.
   b. small intestine.
   c. large intestine.

5. Complex proteins in the liver that catalyze chemical reactions are
   a. enzymes.
   b. metabolites.
   c. antagonists.
   d. nephrons.

6. _____ refers to the transfer of drug into the blood from an administered drug product.
   a. Absorption
   b. Excretion
   c. Distribution
   d. Metabolism

7. "First-pass metabolism" occurs at the
   a. stomach.
   b. kidney.
   c. liver.
   d. small intestine.

8. The main functional unit of the kidney is the/an
   a. glomerulus.
   b. enzyme.
   c. metabolite.
   d. nephron.

9. The body's process of transforming drugs is called
   a. distribution.
   b. metabolism.
   c. excretion.
   d. absorption.

10. Enterohepatic cycling involves the transfer of drugs and their metabolites from the liver into the
    a. lungs.
    b. peritoneal fluid.
    c. kidneys.
    d. intestine.

11. The _____ filter the blood and remove waste materials from it.
    a. kidneys
    b. liver
    c. gall bladder
    d. small intestine

12. The _____ requires drug manufacturers to perform bioequivalency studies on their products before they are approved for marketing.
    a. DEA
    b. AMA
    c. FDA
    d. United States Pharmacopeia

13. The relative amount of an administered dose that reaches the general circulation and the rate at which this occurs is called
    a. bioavailability.
    b. therapeutic alternative.
    c. bioequivalence.
    d. therapeutic equivalent.

14. Drug products that contain identical amounts of the same active ingredients in the same dosage form are called
    a. alternative drug products.
    b. bioequivalent drug products.
    c. pharmaceutical equivalents.
    d. antagonist drug products.

— 11 —

FACTORS AFFECTING DRUG ACTIVITY

KEY CONCEPTS

Test your knowledge by covering the information in the right hand column.

human variability	Differences in age, weight, genetics, and gender are among the significant factors that influence the differences in medication responses among people.
age	Drug distribution, metabolism, and excretion are quite different in the neonate and infant than in adults because their organ systems are not fully developed. Children metabolize certain drugs more rapidly than adults. The elderly typically consume more drugs than other age groups. They also experience physiological changes that significantly affect drug action.
pregnancy	A number of physiological changes that occur in women in the latter stages of pregnancy tend to reduce the rate of absorption.
genetics	Genetic differences can cause differences in the types and amounts of proteins produced in the body, which can result in differences in drug action.
pharmacogenetics	A new field of study that defines the hereditary basis of individual differences.
weight	Weight adjustments may be needed for individuals whose weight is more than 50% higher than the average adult weight. Weight adjustments are also made for children, or unusually small, emaciated, or obese adult patients.
disease states	The disposition and effect of some drugs can be altered in one person but not in another by the presence of diseases other than the one for which a drug is used. Hepatic, cardiovascular, renal, and endocrine disease all increase the variability in drug response. For example, decreased blood flow from cardiovascular disorders can delay or cause erratic drug absorption.

allergic reactions   Almost any drug, in almost any dose, can produce an allergic or hypersensitive reaction in a patient. Anaphylactic shock is a potentially fatal hypersensitivity reaction.

common adverse reactions   Anorexia, nausea, vomiting, constipation, and diarrhea are among the most common adverse reactions to drugs.

teratogenicity   The ability of a substance to cause abnormal fetal development when given to pregnant women.

drug–drug interactions   These can result in either increases or decreases in therapeutic effects or adverse effects.

displacement   Displacement of one drug from protein binding sites by a second drug increases the effects of the displaced drug. Decreased intestinal absorption can occur when orally taken drugs combine to produce nonabsorbable compounds, e.g., when magnesium hydroxide and oral tetracycline bind.

enzyme induction   Caused when drugs activate metabolizing enzymes in the liver, increasing the metabolism of other drugs affected by the same enzymes.

enzyme inhibition   When a drug blocks the activity of metabolic enzymes in the liver.

urinary reabsorption   Some drugs raise urinary pH, lessening renal reabsorption, e.g., sodium bicarbonate raises pH and will cause increased elimination of phenobarbital.

additive effects   Occur when two drugs with similar pharmacological actions are taken, e.g., alcohol and a sedative together produce increased sedation.

synergism   Occurs when two drugs with different sites or mechanisms of action produce greater effects than the sum of individual effects, e.g., acetaminophen and aspirin together produce increased anticoagulation.

drug-diet interactions   The physical presence of food in the gastrointestinal tract can alter absorption by interacting chemically (e.g., certain medications and tetracycline); improving the water-solubility of some drugs by increasing bile secretion; affecting the performance of the dosage form (e.g., altering the release characteristics of polymer-coated tablets); altering gastric emptying; altering intestinal movement; altering liver blood flow. Some foods contain substances that react with certain drugs, e.g., foods containing tyramine can react with monoamine oxidase (MAO) inhibitors.

FILL IN THE KEY TERM

Answers are at the end of the book.

additive effects	displacement	idiosyncrasy
adolescent	enzyme inhibition	infant
anaphylactic shock	hepatotoxicity	neonate
carcinogenicity	hypersensitivity	nephrotoxicity
child	hyperthyroidism	synergism
cirrhosis	hypothyroidism	teratogenicity

1. _____ : An abnormal sensitivity generally resulting in an allergic reaction.

2. _____ : A potentially fatal hypersensitivity reaction producing severe respiratory distress and cardiovascular collapse.

3. _____ : An unexpected reaction the first time a drug is taken, generally due to genetic causes.

4. _____ : Toxicity of the liver.

5. _____ : The ability of a substance to harm the kidneys.

6. _____ : The ability of a substance to cause cancer.

7. _____ : The ability of a substance to cause abnormal fetal development when given to pregnant women.

8. _____ : When two drugs with similar pharmacological actions produce greater effects than the sum of individual effects.

9. _____ : The increase in effect when two drugs with similar pharmacological actions are taken equal to the sum of individual effects.

10. _____ : When one drug blocks the activity of metabolic enzymes in the liver.

11. _____ : When one drug is moved from protein binding sites by a second drug, resulting in increased effects of the displaced drug.

12. _____ : A person between the ages of 2 and 12 years.

13. _____ : A person up to one month after birth.

14. _____ : A condition in which thyroid hormone secretions are below normal, often referred to as an underactive thyroid.

15. _____ : A condition in which thyroid hormone secretions are above normal, often referred to as an overactive thyroid.

16. _____ : A person between the ages of 13 and 19 years.

17. _____ : A chronic and potentially fatal liver disease causing loss of function and resistance to blood flow through the liver.

18. _____ : A person between the ages of one month and two years.

True/False

Indicate whether the statement is true or false in the blank. Answers are at the end of the book.

_____ 1. Physiological changes in pregnancy tend to increase the rate of absorption of drugs.

_____ 2. Adults experience a decrease in many physical functions between the ages of 30 and 70 years.

_____ 3. Lower cardiac output in the elderly tends to slow the distribution of drugs.

_____ 4. Foods containing tyramine, such as aged cheeses, may produce dangerous interactions with some medications.

_____ 5. Ibuprofen can cause nephrotoxicity.

_____ 6. Analgesics and antihistamines are not considered teratogenic.

_____ 7. Some anticancer drugs are considered carcinogenic.

_____ 8. Iron salts form nonabsorbable complexes with tetracycline.

_____ 9. If one drug displaces another from a protein binding site, the effects of the displaced drug increase.

_____ 10. Cigarette smoking can affect drug metabolism.

Explain Why

Explain why these statements are true or important. Check your answers in the text. Discuss any questions you may have with your Instructor.

1. Give at least three reasons why drug–drug interactions can increase the effects of drugs.

2. Give at least three reasons why drug–drug interactions can decrease the effects of drugs.

3. Give at least three reasons diet can affect drug activity.

CHOOSE THE BEST ANSWER

Answers are at the end of the book.

1. A potentially fatal allergic reaction is called
   a. nephrotoxicity.
   b. idiosyncrasy.
   c. teratogenicity.
   d. anaphylactic shock.

2. Placebo effects can be due to
   a. pregnancy.
   b. psychological factors.
   c. body weight.
   d. gender.

3. The study of the hereditary basis of individual differences is
   a. lineage.
   b. pharmacoancestry.
   c. pharmacogenetics.
   d. genealogy.

4. Hypersensitivity generally happens because a patient develops
   a. anaphylaxis.
   b. anorexia.
   c. antibodies.
   d. hepatotoxicity.

5. Nephrotoxicity is associated with the
   a. central nervous system.
   b. liver.
   c. kidneys.
   d. small intestine.

6. Unpleasant physical symptoms when some drugs are discontinued is called
   a. psychological dependence.
   b. idiosyncrasy.
   c. anaphylaxis.
   d. physiological dependence.

7. Antineoplastics can cause bone marrow suppression; and this is an example of
   a. hematological effects.
   b. carcinogenicity.
   c. teratogenicity.
   d. nephrotoxicity.

8. The ability of a substance to cause abnormal fetal development when given to pregnant women is called
   a. hematological effects.
   b. idiosyncrasy.
   c. nephrotoxicity.
   d. teratogenicity.

9. _____ occurs when two drugs with similar pharmacological effects produce greater effects than the sum of individual effects when taken together.
   a. Synergism
   b. Additive effects
   c. Interference
   d. Displacement

10. Drugs that increase activity of metabolizing enzymes in the liver cause
    a. glomerular filtration.
    b. enzyme induction.
    c. renal secretion.
    d. enzyme inhibition.

11. A drug given to block or reduce toxic effects of another drug is called a(n)
    a. antidote.
    b. synergist.
    c. inducer.
    d. MAO inhibitor.

12. Urinary reabsorption is a/an _____ process.
    a. active
    b. passive

13. In general, dietary fiber _____ absorption of drugs.
    a. increases
    b. decreases

STUDY NOTES

Use this area to write important points you'd like to remember.

— 12 —

INFORMATION

KEY CONCEPTS

Test your knowledge by covering the information in the right hand column.

primary literature	Original reports of research projects and studies.
secondary literature	General reference works based upon primary literature sources.
tertiary literature	Condensed works based on primary literature.
abstracting services	Services that summarize information from various primary sources for quick reference.
Material Safety Data Sheets (MSDSs)	OSHA required information for handling hazardous chemicals.
state regulations	Many states have Pharmacy Statutes or State Board of Pharmacy Rules and Regulations that require pharmacies to maintain specific professional literature references.
***Drug Facts and Comparisons* (DFC)**	A preferred reference for comprehensive and timely drug information, containing information about prescription and OTC products.
Martindale	"The Extra Pharmacopoeia," contains information on drugs in clinical use internationally.
Physicians' Desk Reference	An annual publication that contains information similar to pharmaceutical manufacturers' drug package inserts.
AHFS Drug Information	The authority for drug information questions. It groups drug monographs by therapeutic use.
USP Pharmacist's Pharmacopeia Product Information	Provides comprehensive information on compounding, packaging, labeling, and storage of pharmaceutical preparations.

Handbook on Injectable Drugs	A collection of monographs on commercially available parenteral drugs that include preparation, storage administration, compatibility, and stability of injectable drugs.
Merck Index	Information on chemicals, drugs, and biologicals including names, chemical structures, and physical and toxicity data.
American Drug Index	A comprehensive list of drug products that contains trade and generic drug names, phonetic pronunciations, indications, manufacturers, and schedule information in a dictionary format.
Red Book	Guide to products and prices, providing annual price lists of drug products including manufacturer, package size, strength, and wholesale and retail prices.
"Orange Book"	The common name for the FDA's *Approved Drug Products with Therapeutic Equivalence Evaluations.*
personal digital assistants (PDAs)	Small hand-held computers that pharmacists can use for drug information.
Internet	A "supernetwork" of many networks from around the world all connected to each other by telephone lines, and all using a common "language."
search engine	Internet software that searches the Web for specific information related to criteria entered by the user.
URL (uniform resource locator)	A web address.

STUDY NOTES

Use this area to write important points or Web addresses you'd like to remember.

Fill in the Key Term

Answers are at the end of the book.

American Hospital Formulary
    Service (AHFS) Drug
    Information
browser
Drug Facts and Comparisons
Handbook on Injectable
    Drugs

Internet Service Provider (ISP)
Martindale
Material Safety Data Sheets
    (MSDS)
Physicians' Desk Reference
primary literature
Red Book

secondary literature
tertiary literature
URL
World Wide Web

1. _____ : Original reports of clinical and other types of research projects and studies.

2. _____ : Condensed works based on primary literature, such as textbooks, monographs, etc.

3. _____ : Reference with updated AWPs and NDCs.

4. _____ : OSHA required information for handling hazardous chemicals.

5. _____ : General reference works based upon primary literature sources.

6. _____ : Accepted as the source of comparative and unbiased drug information. It groups drug monographs by therapeutic use.

7. _____ : A preferred reference for comprehensive and timely drug information, containing information about prescription and OTC products.

8. _____ : Provides information similar to drug package inserts.

9. _____ : A collection of monographs on commercially available parenteral drugs that include topics such as preparation, storage, administration, compatibility, and stability.

10. _____ : A collection of electronic documents at addresses called Web sites.

11. _____ : The "Extra Pharmacopeia" containing international drug monographs.

12. _____ : A software program that allows users to view Web sites on the World Wide Web.

13. _____ : A company that provides access to the Internet.

14. _____ : A web address.

TRUE/FALSE

Indicate whether the statement is true or false in the blank. Answers are at the end of the book.

_____ 1. Primary literature provides the largest amount of and most current source of information.

_____ 2. Abstracting services are considered secondary literature.

_____ 3. *Drug Facts and Comparisons* provides information on prescription and OTC drug products, using comparative tables of therapeutic groups.

_____ 4. *AHFS* is a collection of monographs on parenteral drugs.

_____ 5. *Handbook on Injectable Drugs* is available from USP.

_____ 6. The "Orange Book" is available online.

_____ 7. The *Red Book* provides pricing information.

_____ 8. The *Handbook of Nonprescription Drugs* provides quick access to OTC information.

_____ 9. APhA provides a directory of accredited technician training programs.

_____ 10. Pharmacist Mutual and HPSO are examples of companies that offer pharmacy technicians liability policies.

_____ 11. Certified technicians (CPhTs) must obtain 20 hours of continuing education credits every two years to maintain certification.

EXPLAIN WHY

Explain why these statements are true or important. Check your answers in the text. Discuss any questions you may have with your Instructor.

1. Why is primary literature important?

2. Why is continuing education important?

3. Why should technicians be familiar with pharmaceutical information sources?

4. Why should you know how to use an Internet search engine?

CHOOSE THE BEST ANSWER

Answers are at the end of the book.

1. _____ literature contains condensed works based on primary literature, such as textbooks, monographs, etc.
   a. Orange
   b. Secondary
   c. Tertiary
   d. Abstract

2. OSHA requires pharmacies to have _____ for each hazardous chemical on hand.
   a. manufacturer sheets for documentation of safety
   b. Material Safety Data Sheets (MSDSs)
   c. mixture safety documentation sheets
   d. manufacturer's safety documentation sheets

3. _____ summarize(s) information from primary sources for quick reference.
   a. The PDR
   b. *American Drug Index*
   c. *US Pharmacist*
   d. Abstracting services

4. _____ is an example of a trade journal.
   a. *America's Pharmacist*
   b. *Drugdex*
   c. *Pharmacy Law Digest*
   d. *Pharmacy Times*

5. _____ is a collection of monographs on commercially available parenteral drugs.
   a. The *Merck Index*
   b. The "Orange Book"
   c. *Handbook on Injectable Drugs*
   d. *American Drug Index*

6. _____ is an example of a professional practice journal.
   a. *Today's Technician*
   b. *Pharmacy Times*
   c. *US Pharmacist*
   d. *The Medical Letter*

7. *The Pink Sheet* is an example of a
   a. pink sheet.
   b. trade journal.
   c. professional practice journal.
   d. newsletter.

8. The name of the principal pharmacology text is
   a. Goodman and Gilman's.
   b. *American Drug Index*.
   c. *Micromedex*.
   d. Remington's.

9. A web address is also known as a
   a. url.
   b. dsl.
   c. browser.
   d. isp.

10. Remington, *The Science and Practice of Pharmacy*, is published
    a. annually.
    b. every two years.
    c. every five years.
    d. every ten years.

11. The Website address of the American Pharmacists Association is
    a. www.ashp.org.
    b. www.pharmacist.com.
    c. www.fda.gov.
    d. www.apa.gov.

12. A _____ can be used to search the web for information specified by the user.
   a. modem
   b. browser
   c. search engine
   d. url

13. The _____ provides links to VIPPS.
   a. National Association of Boards of Pharmacy
   b. American Pharmacists Association
   c. American Society of Health-System Pharmacists
   d. Pharmacy Technician Certification Board

14. The Palm Pilot™ is an example of a(n)
   a. LCD.
   b. ISP.
   c. DSL.
   d. PDA.

STUDY NOTES

Use this area to write important points or Web addresses you'd like to remember.

— 13 —

INVENTORY MANAGEMENT

KEY CONCEPTS

Test your knowledge by covering the information in the right hand column.

inventory goals	The goal of inventory management is two-fold: to ensure drugs are available when needed and that contract or special pricing is followed.
open formulary	One that allows purchase of any medication that is prescribed.
closed formulary	A limited list of approved medications.
wholesalers	More than three-quarters of pharmaceutical manufacturers' sales are directly to drug wholesalers, who in turn resell their inventory to hospitals, pharmacies, and other pharmaceutical dispensers. They are government-licensed and regulated.
Schedule II substances	Must be stocked separately in a secure place and require a special order form for reordering. Their stock must be continually monitored and documented.
perpetual inventory	A system that maintains a continuous record of every item in inventory so that it always shows the stock on hand.
spoilage	Inappropriate storage conditions or expired products automatically determine that a product is spoiled since in either case the chemical compounds in the drug product may have degraded.
turnover	The rate at which inventory is used.
point of sale (POS) system	A system in which the item is deducted from inventory as it is sold or dispensed.
drug reorder points	Maximum and minimum inventory levels for each drug.
hard copy	Important reports (especially purchase orders) should be regularly printed out and filed as hard copy both for convenience and as a backup record-keeping system.

computer maintenance	Factors that can damage computer systems are temperature, dust, moisture, movement, vibrations, and power surges.
data back-up	Pharmacy computer files must be regularly backed-up or copied to an appropriate storage media.
order entry device	In a computerized inventory system, a hand-held device to generate orders.
online ordering	In an online ordering system, if an order can be filled as ordered, a message from the supplier will automatically confirm the order to the ordering system. The system automatically assigns to each order a purchase order number for identification.
Material Safety Data Sheets	Instructions for hazardous substances such as chemotherapeutic agents that indicate when special handling and shipping is required.
controlled substance shipping	These substances are shipped separately and checked in by a pharmacist. A special order form must be used for Schedule II substances.
stock bottles	The bulk containers in which most medications are received from the supplier.
storage	Drugs must be stored according to manufacturer's specifications. Most drugs are kept in a fairly constant room temperature of 59°–86°F. The temperature of refrigeration should generally be 36°–46°F.
freshness	Medications should be organized in a way that will dispense the oldest items first.
dispensing units	In hospitals and other settings, medications are stocked in dispensing units throughout the facility that may be called supply stations or med-stations.

STUDY NOTES

Use this area to write important points you'd like to remember.

FILL IN THE KEY TERM

Answers are at the end of the book.

automated dispensing system	order entry device	therapeutic equivalent
closed formulary	perpetual inventory	turnover
dispensing units	purchase order number	unit-dose
inventory	reorder points	
open formulary	Schedule II substances	

1. _____ : One that allows purchase of any medication that is prescribed.

2. _____ : A limited list of approved medications.

3. _____ : The rate at which inventory is used, generally expressed in number of days.

4. _____ : Must be stocked separately in a secure place and require a special order form for reordering. Their stock must be continually monitored and documented.

5. _____ : A system that maintains a continuous record of every item in inventory so that it always shows the stock on hand.

6. _____ : A list of goods or items a business uses in its normal operations.

7. _____ : Minimum and maximum stock levels which determine when a reorder is placed and for how much.

8. _____ : In a computerized inventory system, a hand-held device to generate orders.

9. _____ : Pharmaceuticals that have the same effect in patients.

10. _____ : A number assigned to each order for products that will allow it to be tracked and checked throughout the order process.

11. _____ : Medications are dispensed at their point of use after an order has been confirmed and then communicated from a centralized computer system.

12. _____ : A package containing a single dose of a medication.

13. _____ : In hospitals and other settings, medications are stocked in units throughout the facility that may also be called supply stations or med-stations.

TRUE/FALSE

Indicate whether the statement is true or false in the blank. Answers are at the end of the book.

_____ 1.   The majority of pharmaceutical manufacturer sales are to wholesalers.

_____ 2.   Baker Cells® is an example of a robotic device.

_____ 3.   Reorder points are maximum and minimum inventory levels for a product.

_____ 4.   Computerized ordering systems do not allow manual editing.

_____ 5.   Point-of-sale systems adjust inventory as medications are sold or dispensed.

_____ 6.   With computers keeping records, printed copies are not needed.

_____ 7.   Certain hazardous substances may not be shipped by air.

_____ 8.   A closed formulary allows any medication prescribed to be purchased.

_____ 9.   Most drug products should be stored at 50°–59°.

_____ 10. Hospitals frequently use drug dispensing units located at points of use throughout the hospital.

EXPLAIN WHY

Explain why these statements are true or important. Check your answers in the text. Discuss any questions you may have with your Instructor.

1.   Why are wholesalers used?

2.   Why is knowing the turnover rate of a product important?

3.   Why are reorder points used?

4.   Why is it important to make hard copy of computerized reports?

5.   Why is it important to back up computer files?

CHOOSE THE BEST ANSWER

Answers are at the end of the book.

1. The list of medications that are approved for use in a health-care system is called a(an)
   a. turnover.
   b. formulary.
   c. therapeutic equivalent.
   d. wholesaler.

2. Medications that are chemically different but have similar actions and effects are
   a. generic equivalents.
   b. always less expensive.
   c. always more expensive.
   d. therapeutically equivalent.

3. _____ is an expression for the rate at which inventory is used and is generally expressed in number of days.
   a. Reciprocal
   b. Turnover
   c. POS
   d. Availability

4. Large purchasing groups that buy drugs in bulk for their members are called
   a. GPOs.
   b. wholesalers.
   c. OSHA.
   d. DOT.

5. Pyxis Med/Supply Station® is a good example of a(n)
   a. automated point-of-use storage system.
   b. automated dispensing machine.
   c. robotic dispensing machine.
   d. mobile robot.

6. Material Safety Data Sheets (MSDS) are required by _____ for hazardous substances and provide hazard, handling, clean-up, and first aid information.
   a. OSHA
   b. State Board of Pharmacy
   c. FDA
   d. DEA

7. When reconciling an order, controlled substances are shipped separately, and should be checked in by a(an)
   a. technician.
   b. pharmacy clerk.
   c. pharmacist.
   d. intern.

8. An inventory system in which the item is deducted from inventory as it is dispensed is called a/an
   a. automated dispensing unit.
   b. point-of-use system.
   c. formulary.
   d. point of sale system (POS).

9. The p.o. number identifies the
   a. post office.
   b. pharmacy.
   c. point-of-sale.
   d. purchase order.

10. Walkers, wheel chairs, crutches, and bedpans are examples of
    a. GPO.
    b. DME.
    c. DOT.
    d. EPA.

STUDY NOTES

Use this area to write important points you'd like to remember.

— 14 —

FINANCIAL ISSUES

KEY CONCEPTS

Test your knowledge by covering the information in the right hand column.

third party programs
Another party besides the patient or the pharmacy that pays for some or all of the cost of medication: essentially, an insurer.

pharmacy benefit manager (PBM)
A company that administers drug benefit programs for insurance companies, HMOs, and self-insured employers.

co-insurance
Essentially an agreement between the insurer and the insured to share costs.

co-pay
The portion of the cost of prescriptions that patients with third party insurance must pay.

deductible
A set amount that must be paid by the patient for each benefit period before the insurer will cover additional expenses.

maximum allowable cost (MAC)
The amount paid by the insurer is not equal to the retail price normally charged, but is determined by a formula described in a contract between the insurer and the pharmacy. There is a maximum allowable cost (MAC) per tablet or other dispensing unit that an insurer or PBM will pay for a given product.

usual and customary (U&C)
The MAC is often determined by survey of the usual and customary (U&C) prices for a prescription within a given geographic area. This is also referred to as the UCR (usual, customary, and reasonable) price for the prescription.

prescription drug benefit cards
Cards that contain necessary billing information for pharmacies, including the patient's identification number, group number, and co-pay amount.

HMO (health maintenance organization)
Health care networks that usually do not cover expenses incurred outside the network and often require generic substitution.

point of service (POS)	Health care network where the patient's primary care physician must be a member and costs outside the network may be partially reimbursed.
preferred provider organization (PPO)	Health care network that reimburses expenses outside the network at a lower rate than inside the network and usually requires generic substitution.
workers' compensation	Compensation for employees accidentally injured on-the-job.
Medicare	National health insurance for people over the age of 65, disabled people under the age of 65, and people with kidney failure.
Medicaid	A federal-state program for the needy.
online adjudication	Most prescription claims are now filed electronically by online claim submission and online adjudication of claims. In online adjudication, the technician uses the computer to determine the exact coverage for each prescription with the appropriate third party.
dispense as written (DAW)	When brand name drugs are dispensed, numbers corresponding to the reason for submitting the claim with brand name drugs are entered in a DAW (dispense as written) indicator field in the prescription system.
patient identification number	The number assigned to the patient by the insurer that is indicated on the drug benefit card. If it does not match the code for the patient in the insurer's computer (with the same sex and other information) a claim may be rejected.
age limitations	Many prescription drug plans have age limitations for children or dependents of the cardholder.
refills	Most third party plans require that most of the medication has been taken before the plan will cover a refill of the same medication.
maintenance medications	Many managed care health programs require mail order pharmacies to fill prescriptions for maintenance medications.
rejected claims	When a claim is rejected, the pharmacy technician can telephone the insurance plan's pharmacy help desk to determine if the patient is eligible for coverage.

FILL IN THE KEY TERM

Answers are at the end of the book.

co-insurance
co-pay
deductible
dual co-pay
CMS1500 form (formerly
   HCFA 1500 form)
CPT code

HMO
maximum allowable
   cost (MAC)
Medicaid
Medicare
online adjudication
patient assistance programs

pharmacy benefits managers
POS
PPO
prescription drug benefit cards
U&C or UCR
universal claim form
workers' compensation

1. _____ : Companies that administer drug benefit programs.

2. _____ : The resolution of prescription coverage through the communication of the pharmacy computer with the third party computer.

3. _____ : An agreement for cost-sharing between the insurer and the insured.

4. _____ : The portion of the price of medication that the patient is required to pay.

5. _____ : Co-pays that have two prices: one for generic and one for brand medications.

6. _____ : The maximum price per tablet (or other dispensing unit) an insurer or PBM will pay for a given product.

7. _____ : The maximum amount of payment for a given prescription, determined by the insurer to be a reasonable price.

8. _____ : A network of providers for which costs are covered inside but not outside of the network.

9. _____ : A network of providers where the patient's primary care physician must be a member and costs outside the network may be partially reimbursed.

10. _____ : A network of providers where costs outside the network may be partially reimbursed and the patient's primary care physician need not be a member.

11. _____ : A set amount that must be paid by the patient for each benefit period before the insurer will cover additional expenses.

12. _____ : Cards that contain third party billing information for prescription drug purchases.

13. _____ : Identifiers used for billing pharmacist-provided MTMS.

14. _____ : A federal program providing health care to people with certain disabilities over age 65.

15. _____ : A federal-state program, administered by the states, providing health care for the needy.

16. _____ : The standard form used by health care providers to bill for services.

17. _____ : An employer compensation program for employees accidentally injured on the job.

18. _____ : Manufacturer sponsored prescription drug programs for the needy.

19. _____ : A standard claim form accepted by many insurers for billing drugs.

TRUE/FALSE

Indicate whether the statement is true or false in the blank. Answers are at the end of the book.

_____ 1. The amount paid by a co-insurer to the pharmacy is equal to the wholesale price of a drug.

_____ 2. In online adjudication, the claim processing computer determines if the claim is valid and what the co-pay should be, usually in less than a minute.

_____ 3. A pharmacy benefits manager is a company that administers drug benefits programs.

_____ 4. A dual co-pay means that the patient will pay a different co-pay for generic and brand drugs.

_____ 5. Many third-party programs have drug formularies.

_____ 6. The CPT code for billing an initial patient encounter for pharmacist-provided services is 99605.

_____ 7. All Medicaid programs have an open formulary.

_____ 8. An NPI number identifies the pharmacy.

EXPLAIN WHY

Explain why these statements are true or important. Check your answers in the text. Discuss any questions you may have with your Instructor.

1. If an online claim is rejected, why is it important to review the information that was originally entered before calling?

2. Why is it important to know the benefits of various third party programs?

CHOOSE THE BEST ANSWER

Answers are at the end of the book.

1. The resolution of prescription coverage for a prescription through the communication of the pharmacy computer with the third party computer is called
   a. PBM.
   b. online adjudication.
   c. MAC.
   d. UCR.

2. The Maximum Allowable Cost (MAC) is usually _____ the Usual and Customary (U&C) price.
   a. less than
   b. greater than
   c. equal to

3. A(an) _____ is a set amount that must be paid by the patient before the insurer will cover additional expenses.
   a. co-insurance
   b. co-pay
   c. maximum allowable cost
   d. deductible

4. A(an) _____ is a network of providers where the patient's primary care physician must be a member and costs outside the network may be partially reimbursed.
   a. HMO
   b. POS
   c. PPO
   d. MAC

5. _____ is a program for people over age 65 or with certain disabilities.
   a. Medicaid
   b. ADC
   c. Workers' Compensation
   d. Medicare

6. The optional Medicare program with prescription drug coverage is
   a. Medicare Part A.
   b. Medicare Part B.
   c. Medicare Part C.
   d. Medicare Part D.

7. Procedures for billing compounded prescriptions
   a. should always be referred to the pharmacist.
   b. are not available.
   c. do not apply in community pharmacy practice.
   d. are variable, depending on the insurer or PBM.

8. When a technician receives a rejected claim "invalid birth date," this probably means
   a. the patient has Medicaid.
   b. the patient does not have coverage.
   c. the birth date submitted by the pharmacy does not match the birth date in the insurer's computer.
   d. the patient has Medicare.

9. The form used by health-care providers to apply for a National Provider Identifier (NPI) is
   a. CMS-1500.
   b. CMS-10114.
   c. a universal claim form.
   d. CPT 0116T.

10. _____ services are provided by pharmacists to some patients enrolled in Medicare Part D.
    a. MTM.
    b. PDP.
    c. CPT.
    d. NPI.

STUDY NOTES

Use this area to write important points you'd like to remember.

— 15 —

COMMUNITY PHARMACY

KEY CONCEPTS

Test your knowledge by covering the information in the right hand column.

community pharmacy

The pharmacy practice that provides prescription services to the public. In addition to prescription drugs, community pharmacies sell over-the-counter medications as well as other health and beauty products. In the United States, more than half of all prescription drugs are dispensed by community pharmacies. There are about 60,000 community pharmacies.

counseling

The role of the community pharmacist in counseling and educating patients has been steadily increasing. In the United States, the 1990 Omnibus Budget and Reconciliation Act (OBRA) required community pharmacists to offer counseling to Medicaid patients regarding medications. Many states have expanded this requirement to apply to all customers.

regulation

Community pharmacies are most closely regulated at the state level. In addition to the many regulations on prescribers and prescriptions, states regulations include such things as the ratio of pharmacists to technicians, scope of practice, record keeping, equipment, and work areas.

customer service

A major area of importance in the community pharmacy, since technicians constantly interact with patients as customers. It is important to always respond to customers in a positive and courteous way.

interpersonal skills

Skills involving relationships between people. Good interpersonal skills are based on techniques such as looking the other person in the eye, listening carefully, etc.

telephone use

Telephone calls must be answered in a pleasant and courteous manner, following a standard format that should be indicated by the store manager or pharmacist.

refills	When processing a refill prescription, it is necessary to check that there are refills available. In the case of a patient requesting an early refill of a controlled substance, involve the pharmacist right away.
drug interactions	Whenever the prescription system flags drug interactions and allergy conflicts, alert the pharmacist so that he or she can evaluate the significance of the flag.
safety caps	All dispensed prescription vials and bottles must have a safety cap or child resistant cap, unless the patient requests an easy-open or non-child resistant cap.
auxiliary labels	Auxiliary labels identify important usage information, including specific warnings or alerts on: administration, proper storage, possible side effects, and potential food and drug interactions.
final check by pharmacist	As a final step of the prescription preparation process, the final product and all paperwork, including the original prescription, is organized for the pharmacist's final check.
signature log	Customer signatures in a log are required for Medicaid and most third party insurer or HMO prescriptions, along with Schedule V controlled substances, poisons, and certain other prescriptions (depending upon the state).
mark-up	The amount of the retailer's sale price minus their purchase price. It is calculated by multiplying the retailer's purchase price by the mark-up percentage. For example, a 30% mark-up on an item purchased for $2.30 is $0.69 (2.30 x 0.3), so the sale price would be $2.99.
OTC products	Drug products that do not require a prescription, but are not without risks. Therefore, the technician should not recommend them to pharmacy customers.
shelf stickers	Stickers for OTC drugs and other products that can be scanned for inventory identification.
unit price	The price of a single unit of a product, such as for one ounce of a liquid cold remedy.
stock	Managing stock is often a technician responsibility and includes ordering, receiving, storing, and placing products on shelves.
Disease State Management Services	Programs that provide one-on-one pharmacist-patient consultation sessions to help manage chronic diseases or conditions.

IN THE WORKPLACE

Use these tools to practice and check some of your workplace skills.

Pharmacy Technician Skills Checklist
BASIC COMPUTER ENTRY SKILLS

Name: _____

Skill or Procedure	Self-Assessment		Supervisor Review		
	Needs to Improve	Meets or Exceeds	Needs to Improve*	Meets or Exceeds	*Plan of Action
1. Properly interprets medical abbreviations.					
2. Understands dosage forms.					
3. Understands prescription number assignments (controlled, non-controlled).					
4. Properly enters a new patient into computer.					
5. Properly adds a new patient to an existing family file.					
6. Properly uses SIG codes.					
7. Properly adds medication allergy codes.					
8. Properly processes refill prescriptions using computer.					
9. Understands procedures for DUR screens.					
10. Properly enters third party billing (insurance) information.					
11. Properly adds a new doctor file (if doctor is not already in the database).					
12. Chooses correct drug (matches NDC).					
13. Uses appropriate DAW codes.					

Name: _____

Pharmacy Technician Skills Checklist
GENERAL COMPUTER ENTRY SKILLS

Skill or Procedure	Self-Assessment		Supervisor Review		
	Needs to Improve	Meets or Exceeds	Needs to Improve*	Meets or Exceeds	*Plan of Action
1. Properly puts new prescriptions on file (without filling).					
2. Enters and uses alternate third party plans.					
3. Enters compounded prescriptions.					
4. Generates daily reports.					
5. Generates medical expense statements.					
6. Updates inventories.					
7. Updates order quantities.					

FILL IN THE KEY TERM

Answers are at the end of the book.

auxiliary labels
counting tray
Disease State Management
    Services
group number
HIPAA

interpersonal skills
OBRA
patient identification number
refrigeration
safety caps
signature log

scope of practice
shelf stickers
transaction windows
unit price

1. _____ : Required community pharmacists to offer counseling to Medicaid patients regarding medications.

2. _____ : Based on techniques such as looking the other person in the eye, listening carefully, etc.

3. _____ : What technicians may and may not do, as mandated by their state.

4. _____ : Counter areas designated for taking prescriptions and for delivering them to patients.

5. _____ : Temperature should be between 2°–8°C (36°–46°F).

6. _____ : The number of the patient's insurance policy as indicated on their drug benefit card.

7. _____ : A number that identifies a patient's employer.

8. _____ : A book or electronic device to provide verification that a prescription was picked up.

9. _____ : Required all health care providers to protect patient privacy.

10. _____ : Child resistant caps required of all dispensed prescription vials.

11. _____ : A tray designed for counting pills.

12. _____ : Stickers with bar codes that can be scanned for inventory identification.

13. _____ : Provide one-on-one pharmacist-patient consultation to help manage chronic diseases and conditions.

14. _____ : Labels regarding specific warnings and usage information.

15. _____ : For example, the price for one ounce of a liquid cold remedy.

TRUE/FALSE

Indicate whether the statement is true or false in the blank. Answers are at the end of the book.

_____ 1.   More than half of all drugs in the U.S. are sold at community pharmacies.

_____ 2.   Many states put limits on the number of technicians assisting the pharmacist at a given time.

_____ 3.   The pharmacy technician should not recommend OTC products to pharmacy customers.

_____ 4.   The DAW code is only required for controlled substance prescriptions.

_____ 5.   HIPAA regulations do not apply to disease state management services provided by pharmacists.

_____ 6.   Safety caps are not used for patients who request an easy open cap.

_____ 7.   Schedule II controlled substance orders must be checked and signed for by the pharmacist.

_____ 8.   When a technician prepares a prescription, it is always checked by the pharmacist before dispensing to the patient.

_____ 9.   Signature logs serve as proof to third-party payers that the prescription was dispensed to the patient.

_____ 10. OTC products may be purchased without a prescription because they are without risk.

_____ 11. Walk-in clinics are usually staffed by nurse practitioners.

EXPLAIN WHY

Explain why these statements are true or important. Check your answers in the text. Discuss any questions you may have with your Instructor.

1.   Why is the health of customers a factor in community pharmacy?

2.   Why are good interpersonal skills important in community pharmacy?

3.   Why is it important to look a patient in the eye and restate what they have said?

4.   Why does the pharmacist check technician filled prescriptions before dispensing to patients?

5.   Why shouldn't technicians recommend OTC products?

CHOOSE THE BEST ANSWER

Answers are at the end of the book.

1. Community pharmacies within stores like Walmart or KMart, that are part of regional or national mass merchandise chains are
   a. chain pharmacies.
   b. mass merchandiser pharmacies.
   c. independent pharmacies.
   d. food store pharmacies.

2. Customer service is a major area of importance in _____ compared to _____.
   a. community pharmacy, institutional pharmacy
   b. hospital pharmacy, institutional pharmacy
   c. institutional pharmacy, community pharmacy
   d. institutional pharmacy, hospital pharmacy

3. The refrigerator in a community pharmacy must store medications between
   a. 2° and 8° Fahrenheit.
   b. 32° and 40° Celsius.
   c. 2° and 8° Celsius.
   d. 32° and 40° Fahrenheit.

4. Medicare Part D relies on _____ to provide medication coverage to eligible patients.
   a. Medicaid
   b. Patient Assistance Programs
   c. Prescription Drug Plans
   d. state welfare programs

5. If a patient is requesting a refill, the technician should be sure to obtain the
   a. patient's name and prescription number.
   b. correct drug and strength, correct physician's name, directions for use, quantity, number of refills, DAW code, and initials of the dispensing pharmacist.

6. The final check of a new prescription is performed by
   a. the pharmacist.
   b. the prescribing physician.
   c. a certified technician.
   d. the senior technician.

7. OTC product recommendations should be made by
   a. certified technicians.
   b. technicians with seniority.
   c. pharmacists.
   d. technicians with more than two years of experience.

8. When receiving orders for Schedule II controlled substances, they must be checked and signed by the
   a. certified pharmacy technician.
   b. pharmacy technician.
   c. pharmacist.
   d. third party.

9. The primary card holder is usually designated by the patient code
   a. 00.
   b. 01.
   c. 02.
   d. 03.

10. Periodically, counting trays and the pharmacy counter should be wiped with
    a. alcohol.
    b. soap and water.
    c. water.
    d. oil.

STUDY NOTES

Use this area to write important points you'd like to remember.

— 16 —

HOSPITAL PHARMACY

KEY CONCEPTS

Test your knowledge by covering the information in the right hand column.

pharmacist supervision	Pharmacy technicians in the hospital work under the direct supervision of a pharmacist. Only a pharmacist may verify orders in the computer system and check medications being sent to the nursing floors.
patient care units	Patient rooms are divided into groups called nursing units or patient care units, with patients having similar problems often located on the same unit.
nurse's station	The work station for medical personnel on a nursing unit is called the nurse's station. Various items required for care of patients are stored there, including patient medications.
ancillary areas	Areas such as the emergency room that also use medications and are serviced by the pharmacy department.
cart fill	In hospitals that have manual cart fill, medication carts contain a 24-hour supply of medications in a patient cassette or drawer.
delivery technician	A delivery technician is responsible for transporting medications and other pharmacy supplies from the pharmacy to nursing units, ancillary areas of the hospital, and/or outpatient clinics.
central pharmacy	The main inpatient pharmacy in a hospital that has pharmacy satellites.
pharmacy satellite	A branch of the inpatient pharmacy responsible for preparing, dispensing, and monitoring medication for specific patient areas.
investigational drug service	A specialized pharmacy subsection that deals solely with clinical drug trials. These drug studies require a great deal of

paperwork and special documentation of all doses of study medication taken by patients. Technicians frequently assist the pharmacist with this documentation and in preparing individual patient medication supplies.

formulary

A list of drugs stocked at the hospital which have been selected based on therapeutic factors as well as cost.

closed formulary

A closed formulary requires physicians to order medications from the formulary list.

non-formulary

Drugs not on the formulary list.

patient-specific trays

The amount of medications for a 24 hour period are placed in patient trays that are loaded into medication carts.

unit dose

A package containing the amount of drug for one dose.

pre-packing

Technicians often "pre-pack" medications that have been supplied in bulk into unit doses. Machines that automate this process are generally used for pre-packing oral solid medications.

unit dose labels

Unit dose labels contain bar codes for identification and control. Items are scanned into the dispensing and inventory system at various stages up to dispensing. This reduces the chances of medication errors and improves documentation and inventory control.

medication order form

In the hospital, all drugs ordered for a patient are written on a medication order form and not a prescription blank as in a community pharmacy. Physicians write medication orders for hospital patients, though both nurses and pharmacists may also write orders if they are directly instructed to do so by a doctor. In addition, physician's assistants and nurse practitioners may sometimes write orders, depending upon the institution.

medication administration record

Nurses record and track medication orders on a patient specific form called the medication administration record (MAR).

computerized physician order entry (CPOE)

A computer system that allows the physician to enter the medication order directly into the hospital computer system.

controlled substances

A primary area of concern for inventory control is narcotics, or controlled substances, which require an exact record of the location of every item to the exact tablet or unit.

KEY CONCEPTS

Test your knowledge by covering the information in the right hand column.

IV admixtures	A large portion of the medication used in the hospital is administered intravenously. Pharmacy technicians prepare I.V. admixtures, including small and large volume parenterals, parenteral nutrition therapy, and chemotherapy.
code cart	Locked cart filled with emergency medications. All patient care areas are required to have code carts.
policy and procedures manual	A manual containing information about every aspect of the job from dress code to disciplinary actions and step by step directions on how to perform various tasks that will be required of technicians. All departments within the hospital are required by regulating agencies to maintain this.
JCAHO	The Joint Commission on Accreditation of Healthcare Organizations, the accreditation agency for healthcare organizations. Organizations undergo a JCAHO survey every 3 years.
sharps container	Needles or other items that may cut or puncture the skin should always be thrown away in designated sharps containers.

unit dose medications

patient trays

MEDICATION ORDERS

Medication order forms are an all-purpose communication tool used by the various members of the healthcare team. Orders for various procedures, laboratory tests, and x-rays may be written on the form in addition to medication orders. Several medication orders may be written on one medication order form unlike pharmacy prescription blanks seen in the retail setting.

There are several different types of orders that can be written. One is a standard medication order for patients to receive a certain drug at scheduled intervals throughout the day, sometimes called a standing order. Orders for medications that are administered only on an as needed basis are called PRN medication orders. A third type of order is for a medication that is needed right away and these are referred to as STAT orders.

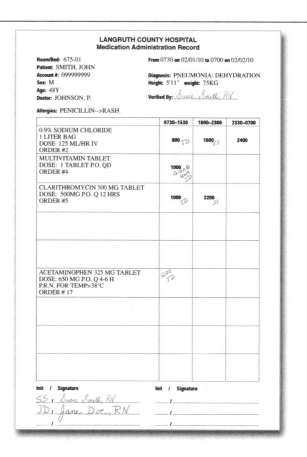

MEDICATION ADMINISTRATION RECORD

On this form every medication ordered for a patient is written down as well as the time it is administered and the person who gave the dose. These forms may be handwritten by the nursing staff or generated by the pharmacy computer system. The MAR is an important document in tracking the care of the patient as it gives a 24 hour picture of a patient's medication use. The accuracy of this document is crucial.

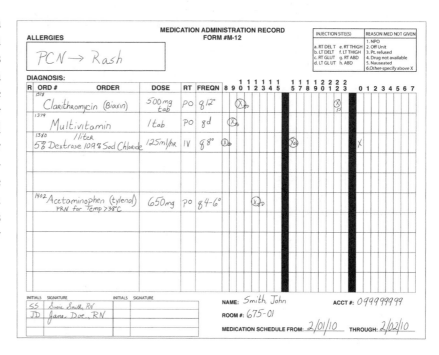

IN THE WORKPLACE

Some questions to ask when entering or checking a medication order.

Several questions should always be asked when entering or checking a medication order.

Question:	Problem	Solution*
✓ Is the patient allergic to the ordered medication or a component of the ordered medication?	A medication order is placed for trimethoprim/sulfamoxazole (Bactrim®), but the patient has a "sulfa" allergy with the description of the allergy stating "hives".	The order should not be processed and a new medication order for a different antibiotic is required.
✓ Is the drug appropriate?	A patient is ordered a potassium IVPB. The most recent potassium lab level = 5 mEq/mL (normal potassium = 3.5 to 5.5 mEq/mL). The medication is not indicated for this patient.	The physician should be notified that the medication is not indicated based on the current lab level.
✓ Is the dose and frequency appropriate?	An order for a patient reads, "Digoxin 0.5 mg po q 6 H." The normal dosing for digoxin is 0.125 – 0.25 mg daily.	The ordered dose would be toxic. The order should be changed.
✓ Has the drug dose/frequency been adjusted for the patient's age, weight, disease state, kidney or liver function?	A 79 year old patient with major renal dysfunction has a new medication order for Fluconazole 400 mg IV daily. Fluconazole is eliminated renally and should be adjusted for renal dysfunction.	The patient's renal function should be calculated and the dose adjusted appropriately.
✓ Is the drug formulation and route most appropriate for the patient?	A patient has an order for an IV medication but the patient is tolerating oral feeds.	Discuss with the physician and change the drug to the oral formulation.
✓ Are there any drug interactions that require changes in the order or increased monitoring that the physician should be made aware?	A new order for amiodarone is received for a patient who is also on warfarin. There is an interaction between amiodarone and warfarin which increases the risk for the patient to bleed.	The physician should be made aware of the interaction and recommended to monitor the patient more closely.
✓ Does the new order therapeutically duplicate another drug the patient is already taking?	A medication order for pantoprazole is ordered for a patient with currently active order for omeprazole. Both medications are proton pump inhibitors and work in the same way.	There would be no additive effect to using both medications. The order needs to be clarified with the physician and one of the orders discontinued.
✓ Is the drug on the hospital formulary? If not, can the medication be therapeutically interchanged?	Famotidine 20mg BID is ordered but the formulary H₂-blocker is ranitidine.	A therapeutic substitution is made to ranitidine 150 mg BID per hospital protocol.
✓ Is the medication "restricted" and need approval from a specific service in the hospital?	Vancomycin 1 g IV q 12 H is ordered for a patient. Vancomycin is restricted by the infectious disease service and it has not yet been approved for this patient.	The infectious disease service should be notified and approval received before processing the order.
✓ Should the medication be limited to a certain number of days due to hospital policy or an automatic stop order?	An order is written for ketoralac 30 mg IV q 6H x 10 days. Hospital policy and manufacturer recommendations limit the length of therapy to 5 days.	The order is changed to 5 days of therapy.

*Unless there is a hospital policy in place to the contrary, all changes in medication orders need to be authorized by the physician before they are changed.

IN THE WORKPLACE

A sample extemporaneous compounding worksheet.

Extemporaneous Compounding Work sheet
Department of Pharmacy
University Medical Center

NAME OF PRODUCT: OMEPRAZOLE ORAL SUSPENSION 2 mg/mL

Hospital Lot No: _____   **Prepared on:** ___ / ___ / ___   **Expires on:** ___ / ___ / ___

INGREDIENTS	MFR	LOT #	EXP DATE	QUANTITY	MADE BY	CHKD BY
Omeprazole (Prilosec®) 20 mg capsules				5		
Sodium Bicarbonate 8.4% (1 mEq/mL)				q.s. 50 mL		

Compounding Instructions:
1. Empty capsules into beaker.
2. Add sodium bicarbonate solution.
3. Gently stir (about 15 minutes) until a white suspension is formed.
4. Transfer to amber-colored bottle.

Stability:
45 days at 4°C

Auxiliary Labels required:
SHAKE WELL
REFRIGERATE
PROTECT FROM LIGHT

References:
Ann Pharmacother, 2000;34:600-605.
Am J Health Syst Pharm, 1999;56(suppl 4): S18-21

IN THE WORKPLACE

A sample orientation checklist.

UNIVERSITY MEDICAL CENTER
Orientation Checklist

NAME: _____ POSITION: _____ HIRE DATE: _____

Pharmacy ORIENTATION SKILL CHECKLIST (outline of competency requirements)	EVALUATION			
	Reviewed (date/initial)	Verbalizes Understanding (date/initial)	Demonstrates Skill (date/initial)	COMMENTS
INTRODUCTION AND TOUR Introduce to all personnel				
Tour pharmacy department - Central pharmacy and pharmacy satellites				
Tour main pathways from department to different areas in hospital				
GENERAL INFORMATION Mailbox				
Phone etiquette/personal calls				
Regular and Holiday schedule				
Vacation and Sick time off				
Time clock (punching in/out)				
PERSONAL NEEDS Dress code				
Cloak storage/locker				
Lunch and coffee breaks				
SECURITY AND SAFETY Exposure control				
Proper waste disposal				
Material Safety Data Sheets (MSDS)				
Mass Casualty Disaster Plan				
COMPUTER ENVIRONMENT / ORDER PROCESSING Computer system (CPOE, Entry and Retrieval, Allergy, Patient Profiles, etc.)				
Order Verification (R.Ph. only)				
Printing labels				
Filling orders				
Managing missing doses				
Delivery schedule/tube system				
Restocking automated dispensing cabinets				
Down-time procedures				
POLICY AND PROCEDURE MANUAL Receipt of manual				
EMPLOYEE HANDBOOK Receipt of handbook				
JOB DESCRIPTION **PERFORMANCE EVALUATION**				

Pharmacy ORIENTATION SKILL CHECKLIST (outline of competency requirements)	EVALUATION			
	Reviewed (date/initial)	Verbalizes Understanding (date/initial)	Demonstrates Skill (date/initial)	COMMENTS
IV SOLUTIONS				
Clean room usage and monitoring				
IV solution preparation procedures				
Aseptic technique				
IV Scheduling – 12-hour batching				
IV area restocking routine				
Total Parenteral Nutrition solutions				
Chemotherapy preparation				
Checking IV solutions (RPh only)				
IV admixture infection control consideration				
MISCELLANEOUS				
Narcotic replenishment				
Narcotic delivery/Narcotics in IV Rom				
Inventory requests				
Servicing ancillary areas				
Borrowing/lending				
Outpatient pharmacy services – Hours of operation				
Crash cart trays/crash cart re-issue				
Investigational drugs				
Repackaging request				
Ethyl alcohol requisitions				
Inventory check/order process				
Requisitioning from General Stores and Materials Management				
Restricted drug programs/Approvals				
On-call coordinator, clinical staff, Pharmacist-In-Charge				
Non-formulary drugs				
Pager system				
Unit-dose cassette process and exchange (Adults/Peds)				

37-0111.1

Most hospital pharmacies utilize a "Pharmacy Technician Orientation Checklist." Once each skill has been demonstrated, the checklist is initialed by the technician and the supervisor. Upon completion it is placed in the pharmacy technician's personnel file.

FILL IN THE KEY TERM

Answers are at the end of the book.

central pharmacy   inpatient pharmacy   policy and procedure manual
clean rooms   medication administration   PRN order
code carts   record (MAR)   reconstitute
demographics   outpatient pharmacy   standing order
electronic medical record   pharmacy satellite   STAT order
final filter   pneumatic tube system   unit dose

1. _____ : Addition of water or other diluent to a powdered drug form to make a solution or suspension.

2. _____ : Non-medical personal identification information about a patient.

3. _____ : A computerized patient medical record.

4. _____ : A package containing the amount of a drug required for one dose.

5. _____ : A standard medication order for patients to receive medication at scheduled intervals.

6. _____ : An order for medication to be administered only on an as needed basis.

7. _____ : An order for medication to be administered immediately.

8. _____ : A form that tracks the medications administered to a patient.

9. _____ : A locked cart of medications designed for emergency use only.

10. _____ : The main inpatient pharmacy in a hospital that has satellite pharmacies.

11. _____ : A pharmacy located in a hospital which serves only those patients in the hospital and its ancillary areas.

12. _____ : A branch of the inpatient pharmacy.

13. _____ : A system that shuttles objects through a tube using compressed air as the force.

14. _____ : Areas designed for the preparation of sterile products.

15. _____ : A pharmacy attached to a hospital servicing patients who have left the hospital or who are visiting doctors in a hospital outpatient clinic.

16. _____ : Documentation of required policies, procedures, and disciplinary actions in a hospital.

17. _____ : A device used to remove particulate matter.

TRUE/FALSE

Indicate whether the statement is true or false in the blank. Answers are at the end of the book.

_____ 1. An LPN supervises a Nurse Practitioner in the hospital setting.

_____ 2. Orders for medications that are needed immediately are PRN orders.

_____ 3. Technicians often prepare IV admixtures in hospitals.

_____ 4. The pharmacy technician supervisor is often responsible for training technicians.

_____ 5. Lot numbers and expiration dates are not needed in bulk compounding logs.

_____ 6. All departments within a hospital are required to maintain a policy and procedure manual.

_____ 7. The pharmacy inventory staff is often responsible for removal of drug recalls from the pharmacy inventory.

EXPLAIN WHY

Explain why these statements are true or important. Check your answers in the text. Discuss any questions you may have with your Instructor.

1. Why can several medication orders be written on a single medication order form?

2. Why is it important for technicians to be familiar with the policy and procedures manual for their department?

CHOOSE THE BEST ANSWER

Answers are at the end of the book.

1. Preparation of large quantities of unit-dose oral solutions/suspensions or small volume parenterals for future use is called
   a. cart filling.
   b. batching.
   c. bulk compounding.
   d. extemporaneous compounding.

2. The correct temperature for a pharmacy refrigerator is
   a. 40–50°F.
   b. 2–8°C.
   c. 40–50°C.
   d. 2–8°F.

3. A health care provider who is concerned with factors such as a patient's ability to pay for medications is a(an)
   a. Pharm.D.
   b. R.Ph.
   c. N.P.
   d. M.S.W.

4. Most reconstituted drugs expire in
   a. 10–14 days.
   b. 7–10 days.
   c. 24 hours.
   d. 48 hours.

5. A pharmacy attached to a hospital that serves patients who have left the hospital or who are visiting doctors in a hospital outpatient clinic is a/an
   a. in-patient pharmacy.
   b. pharmacy satellite.
   c. central pharmacy.
   d. outpatient pharmacy.

6. Pharmacy technicians working in this satellite require special training and chemotherapy certification from the pharmacy department.
   a. oncology
   b. pediatric
   c. OR
   d. radiology

7. Each individual drawer in a medication cart is filled with
   a. the most commonly used medications for a given floor.
   b. large volume parenteral that do not require patient specific labeling.
   c. controlled substances only.
   d. daily medication for a given patient.

8. The unit-dose package type used or ointments and creams is a/an
   a. plastic blister.
   b. ampule.
   c. tube.
   d. vial.

9. Orders for medications that are needed right away are called
   a. PRN orders.
   b. parenteral.
   c. STAT orders.
   d. standing orders.

10. A locked cart of medications designed for emergency use is called a
    a. PCU.
    b. code cart.
    c. satellite.
    d. IP.

11. Rooms designed for the preparation of sterile products are called
    a. satellites.
    b. clean rooms.
    c. CPs.
    d. PCUs.

12. Which of the following agencies is responsible for approving hospitals so they may receive Medicaid reimbursement?
    a. BOP
    b. JCAHO
    c. HCFA
    d. DPH

STUDY NOTES

Use this area to write important points you'd like to remember.

— 17 —

OTHER ENVIRONMENTS

KEY CONCEPTS

Test your knowledge by covering the information in the right hand column.

mail order pharmacy	Delivery of prescriptions by mail (primarily for maintenance therapy). Mail order pharmacies are generally large scale operations that are highly automated. They use assembly line processing in which each step in the prescription fill process is completed or managed by a person who specializes in that step.
maintenance therapy	Therapy for chronic conditions that include depression, gastrointestinal disorders, heart disease, hypertension, and diabetes.
regulation	Mail order pharmacies must follow federal and state requirements in processing prescriptions, but are not necessarily licensed in each state to which they send medications.
pharmacist review	Pharmacists review mail order prescriptions before and after filling.
online drugstore	A type of mail order pharmacy that uses the internet to advertise and take orders for drugs.
home care	Care in the home, generally supervised by a registered nurse who works with a physician, pharmacist, and others to administer a care plan that involves the patient or another care giver.
home infusion	Infusion administered in the home, the fastest growing area of home health care. The primary therapies provided by home infusion services are: antibiotic therapy, parenteral nutrition, pain management, and chemotherapy.
infusion pumps	Pumps that control infusion. There are pumps for specific therapies or multiple therapies, as well as ambulatory pumps that can be worn by patients.
patient education	In home infusion, the patient or their care giver is educated about their therapy: how to self-administer, monitor, report problems, and so on.

admixture preparation	The same rules apply to preparing parenteral admixtures in the home infusion setting as in the hospital.
long-term care	Facilities that provide care for people unable to care for themselves because of mental or physical impairment. Because of limited resources, most long-term care facilities will contract out dispensing and clinical pharmacy services.
distributive pharmacist	A long-term care pharmacist responsible for making sure patients receive the correct medicines that were ordered.
consultant pharmacist	A long-term care pharmacist who develops and maintains an individualized pharmaceutical plan for every long-term care resident.
emergency kits	Locked kits containing emergency medications, similar to code carts used in hospitals.
automated dispensing systems	Automated units which dispense medications at the point of use.

TRUE/FALSE

Indicate whether the statement is true or false in the blank. Answers are at the end of the book.

_____ 1.   Generally drugs cost less in the U.S. than in Canada.

_____ 2.   Mail order pharmacies are often used to handle maintenance medications.

_____ 3.   Code carts are never found in long-term care facilities.

_____ 4.   Antibiotic therapy is a common home infusion service used in treating AIDS related and other infections.

_____ 5.   On the home care team, the technician works under the supervision of a home care aide.

_____ 6.   In home infusion, waste from chemotherapy and the treatment of AIDS patients can be safely disposed with the patient's other trash.

_____ 7.   Pain management generally applies to the infusion of narcotics for patients with painful terminal illnesses or other types of severe chronic pain.

_____ 8.   In home infusion, the stability of the admixture is a primary concern.

EXPLAIN WHY

Explain why these statements are true or important. Check your answers in the text. Discuss any questions you may have with your Instructor.

1. Why is mail order pharmacy growing so rapidly?

2. Why would maintenance drugs be well suited to mail order delivery?

3. Why is patient education important in home infusion?

4. Why is home infusion growing so rapidly?

5. Why is storage of admixtures an issue in home infusion?

6. Why is hazardous waste an issue in home infusion?

CHOOSE THE BEST ANSWER

Answers are at the end of the book.

1. In the U.S., a mail order pharmacy can provide services to
   a. only the states where the company has pharmacies.
   b. only the state of the main campus.
   c. only the state of the main campus and adjacent states.
   d. any state in the U.S.

2. A medication that is required on a continuing basis for the treatment of a chronic condition is called
   a. PRN medication.
   b. PO medication.
   c. STAT medication.
   d. maintenance medication.

3. Medication counseling for mail order pharmacies is done by
   a. registered nurses.
   b. certified technicians.
   c. nurses.
   d. pharmacists.

4. In some long-term care facilities the medication carts are usually filled with enough medications to last
   a. one week.
   b. one day.
   c. one month.
   d. 24 hours.

5. Medications used from emergency kits in long-term care pharmacies are charged to
   a. the patient.
   b. the pharmacy.
   c. the long-term care facility.
   d. none of the above.

6. The type of infusion therapy that usually involves infusion of narcotics for patients with painful terminal illness or severe chronic pain is called
   a. laxative therapy.
   b. maintenance therapy.
   c. pain management therapy.
   d. infection therapy.

7. Regulation of hazardous waste procedures associated with chemotherapy applies to all of the following EXCEPT:

   a. storage.
   b. disposal.
   c. transportation.
   d. pricing.

8. Which member of the home care team is responsible for educating the patient?

   a. R.Ph.
   b. physician
   c. registered nurse
   d. Pharm.D.

9. The fastest growing area of home health care is

   a. home infusion.
   b. mail order.
   c. long-term care.
   d. hazardous waste.

10. Which of the following activities would NOT be part of the pharmaceutical care plan for home infusion pharmacy?

    a. identification of adverse reactions and interventions
    b. delivery
    c. medication monitoring practices
    d. selection of infusion device

STUDY NOTES

Use this area to write important points you'd like to remember.

— 18 —

COMMON DRUGS & THEIR USES

CLASSIFICATION OF DRUGS

There are thousands of drugs used in pharmacy. A basic familiarity with these drugs and their uses will enhance your skills as a pharmacy technician.

Drugs may be classified in different ways. One way is *based on their main therapeutic indication or action*. An example of such a group name would be **antibiotic**, which describes drugs that work by destroying pathogenic organisms (microorganisms that cause disease). Another example of a group name would be **analgesic**, which describes drugs that are used in the alleviation of pain. Following is a sample list of such group names:

Analgesics
Anesthetic Agents
Anti-infectives
Antineoplastics
Cardiovascular Agents
Dermatologicals
Electrolytic Agents
Gastrointestinal & Urinary
  Tract Agents

Hematological Agents
Hormones & Modifiers
Immunobiologic Agents
Musculoskeletal Agents
Neurological Agents
Ophthalmic & Otic Agents
Psychotropic Agents
Respiratory Agents

Another arrangement of drugs is by *specific classification based on how the drug actually works*. Drugs classified this way generally share these characteristics:

1. similar chemical structure
2. similar mechanism of action
3. similar effects (including side effects)

An example of such a classification is the **cephalosporins**, which is found in the antibiotics group. Drugs in the cephalosporins classification share the above mentioned characteristics with each other but not necessarily with other antibiotics, which may have different characteristics. Another example of such a group would be **xanthine derivatives**, which are found in the bronchodilators group.

Example:

Trade Name	Generic Name	Group	Classification
Keflex	Cephalexin	Antibiotic	Cephalosporin
Theo-Dur	Theophylline	Bronchodilator	Xanthine Derivative

Below is a sample list of such classifications:

Angiotensin Converting Enzyme inhibitors (ACE inhibitors)
α-adrenergic agonists
β-blockers
Calcium channel blockers
Cephalosporins
Corticosteroids
Histamine$_2$ blockers
Loop Diuretics

For national certification exams, you will need to know the main groups of drugs used in the retail and hospital setting. More specific classifications are not emphasized. You will learn most of this information on the job: as you handle these medications over and over again, you'll see which drugs are the most commonly used and which are not.

STUDY TIP — DRUG CARDS

A good way to help you remember the most common drugs used in pharmacy is to create drug cards. Drug cards are easy to make by writing the information from the previous list on small index cards. You can then use these to study until you have memorized the information.

Information needed on your drug card:

1. Trade name of drug

2. Generic name of drug

3. Main indication
   Note: Many drugs have more than one indication. You need to know only the main indication.

KEY CONCEPTS

Test your knowledge by covering the information in the right hand column.

USAN	The United States Adopted Names Council (USAN) designates nonproprietary names for drugs.
drug classes	Group names for drugs that have similar activities or are used for the same type of diseases and disorders.
stems	Common stems or syllables that are used to identify the different drug classes and in making new nonproprietary names. They are approved and recommended by the USAN.
neurotransmitter	Substances that carry the impulses from one neuron to another.
blocker	Another name for an antagonist drug—because antagonists block the action of a neurotransmitter.
homeostasis	The state of equilibrium of the body.
mimetic	Another term for an agonist drug—because agonists imitate or "mimic" the action of the neurotransmitter.
analgesia	A state in which pain is not felt even though a painful condition exists.
anti-pyretic	Reduces fever.
opiate-type analgesics	Drugs related to morphine and codeine that can be habit-forming and are used for pain relief.
narcotic analgesics	Same as opiate-type analgesics.
salicylates	Drugs related to aspirin that are used to relieve mild to moderate pain, and have anti-inflammatory and antipyretic properties.
NSAIDs	Non-steroidal anti-inflammatory drugs that have anti-inflammatory, antipyretic, and analgesic properties.
acetaminophen	A drug that relieves mild to moderate pain and has antipyretic properties.
local anesthetics	Drugs that block pain conduction from peripheral nerves to the central nervous system without causing a loss of consciousness.
surgical anesthesia	The stage of anesthesia in which surgery can be safely conducted.
medullary paralysis	An overdose of anesthesia that paralyzes the respiratory and heart centers of the medulla, leading to death.
antibiotic (antimicrobial)	Drug that destroys microorganisms.

antiviral	Drug that attacks a virus.
antifungal	Drug that destroys fungi or inhibits growth of fungi.
antimycobacterial	Drug that attacks the organisms that cause tuberculosis and leprosy.
antiprotozoal	Drug that destroys protozoa.
anthelmintic	Drug that destroys worms.
bactericidal	Bacteria killing.
bacteriostatic	Bacteria inhibiting.
virustatic	Drug that inhibits the growth of viruses.
antineoplastic	Drug that inhibits new growth of cancer cells.
lymphocyte	A type of white blood cell that releases antibodies that destroy disease cells.
metastasis	When cancer cells spread beyond their original site.
neoplasm	A new and abnormal tissue growth, often referring to cancer cells.
remission	A state in which cancer cells are inactive.
arrhythmia	An abnormal heart rhythm.
cardiac cycle	The contraction and relaxation of the heart that pumps blood through the cardiovascular system.
diastolic pressure	The minimum blood pressure when the heart relaxes; the second number in a blood pressure reading.
electrocardiogram (EKG or ECG)	A graph of the heart's rhythm.
embolism	A clot that has traveled in the bloodstream to a point where it obstructs flow.
myocardium	Heart muscle.
systolic pressure	The maximum blood pressure when the heart contracts; the first number in a blood pressure reading.
thrombus	A blood clot.
antianginals	Drugs used to treat cardiac related chest pain (angina).
antiarrhythmics	Drugs used to treat irregular heart rhythms.
antihypertensives	Drugs used to reduce a sustained elevation in blood pressure.
vasopressors	Drugs used to increase blood pressure.

KEY CONCEPTS

Test your knowledge by covering the information in the right hand column.

antihyperlipidemics	Drugs used to lower high levels of cholesterol.
thrombolytics	Drugs used to dissolve blood clots.
anticoagulants	Drugs used to prevent blood clot formation.
beta blockers	Drugs that reduce the oxygen demands of the heart muscle.
calcium channel blockers	Drugs that relax the heart by reducing heart conduction.
diuretics	Drugs that decrease blood pressure by decreasing blood volume.
ACE inhibitors	The "pril" drugs that relax the blood vessels.
vasodilators	Drugs that relax and expand the blood vessels.
dermatological	A product that is used to treat a skin condition.
integumentary system	The skin.
anion	A negatively charged ion.
cation	A positively charged ion.
dissociation	When a compound breaks down and separates into smaller components.
electrolytes	A substance that in solution forms ions that conduct an electrical current.
extracellular fluids	The fluid outside the body's individual cells found in plasma and tissue fluid.
intracellular fluids	Cell fluid.
interstitial fluid	Tissue fluid.
ions	Electrically charged particles.
vaccine	A suspension containing infectious agents used to boost the body's immune system response.
chime	The semi-liquid form of food as it enters the intestinal tract.
peristalsis	The wave-like motion of the intestines that moves food through them.
enzymes	Substances in the body that help the body to break down molecules.
antidiarrheals	Drugs used to treat diarrhea.
antiemetics	Drugs used to treat nausea and vomiting.

antacids	Drugs used to neutralize acid.
laxatives	Drugs that promote defecation.
stool softeners	Drugs that promote mixing of fatty and watery internal substances to soften the stool's contents and ease the evacuation of feces.
hematological agents	Drugs that affect the blood.
fibrin	The fiber that serves as the structure for clot formation.
anemia	A decrease in hemoglobin or red blood cells.
hemostatic drugs	Drugs that prevent excessive bleeding.
hormones	Chemicals that are secreted in the body by the endocrine system's ductless glands.
corticosteroid	Hormonal steroid substances produced by the cortex of the adrenal gland.
endocrine system	The system of hormone secreting glands.
hyperthyroidism	Overproduction of thyroid hormone.
hypothyroidism	Underproduction of thyroid hormone.
insulin	A hormone that controls the body's use of glucose.
glucagon	A hormone that helps convert amino acid to glucose.
diabetes mellitus	A condition in which the body does not produce enough insulin or is unable to use insulin efficiently.
serum glucose	Blood sugar.
androgens	Male sex hormones.
estrogen	Female sex characteristic hormone that is involved in calcium and phosphorus conservation.
progesterone	Female sex characteristic hormone that is involved in ovulation prevention.
testosterone	The primary androgen (male sex hormone).
gout	A painful inflammatory condition in which excess uric acid accumulates in the joints.
rheumatoid arthritis	A chronic and often progressive inflammatory condition with symptoms that include swelling, feelings of warmth, and joint pain.
osteoarthritis	A disorder characterized by weight-bearing bone deterioration, decreasing range of motion, pain, and deformity.
Parkinson's Disease	A progressive neuromuscular condition.

KEY CONCEPTS

Test your knowledge by covering the information in the right hand column.

Alzheimer's Disease	A progressive dementia condition.
epilepsy	A neurologic disorder characterized by seizures.
migraine headaches	A type of headache associated with possible auras and pain.
ophthalmic agents	Drugs used to treat conditions of the eye.
conjunctivitis	Inflammation of the eyelid lining.
glaucoma	A disorder characterized by high pressure within the eye.
mydriatics	Drugs that dilate the pupil.
sedatives	Drugs that are intended to relax and calm.
hypnotics	Drugs that are intended to induce sleep.
bipolar disorder	A disorder characterized by mood swings.
depression	A disorder characterized by low mood.
asthma	A condition characterized by chronic airway inflammation.
emphysema	A condition associated with chronic airway obstruction.
antihistamines	Drugs that replace histamine at histamine receptor sites.
decongestants	Drugs that cause mucous membrane vasoconstriction.
antitussives	Drugs that are used to treat coughs.
bronchodilators	Drugs that are used to relieve bronchospasm.

Study Notes

Use this area to write important points you'd like to remember.

FILL IN THE BLANKS

Match the drug classifications with the generic drug names. Answers are at the end of the book.

Analgesic   Cardiovascular Agent   Psychotropic Agent
Anesthetic   Dermatological Agent   Respiratory Agent
Antidiabetic   Electrolytic Agent
Anti-infective   Gastrointestinal Agent
Antineoplastic   Musculoskeletal Agent

Generic Name	Drug Classification
1. Albuterol	
2. Alprazolam	
3. Amlodipine	
4. Amoxicillin/Clavulanate	
5. Ampicillin	
6. Atenolol	
7. Atorvastatin	
8. Azithromycin	
9. Carisoprodol	
10. Carvedilol	
11. Cefaclor	
12. Certirizine	
13. Ciprofloxacin	
14. Citalopram	
15. Clarithromycin	
16. Clopidogrel	
17. Clotrimazole/Betamethasone	
18. Diltiazem	
19. Docusate Sodium	
20. Doxazosin	
21. Escitalopram	
22. Fluconazole	

23. Fluticasone _____

24. Furosemide _____

25. Glyburide _____

26. Heparin _____

27. Hydrocortisone Cream _____

28. Ibuprofen _____

29. Insulin _____

30. Lactulose _____

31. Levofloxacin _____

32. Lisinopril _____

33. Loperamide _____

34. Metaprolol _____

35. Nifedipine _____

36. Nitroglycerin _____

37. Omeprazole _____

38. Pantoprazole _____

39. Potassium Chloride _____

40. Propoxyphene _____

41. Sertraline _____

42. Silver Sulfadiazine _____

43. Sodium Chloride _____

44. Tamoxifen _____

45. Tramadol _____

46. Trimethobenzamide _____

47. Trimethoprim/Sulfamethoxazole _____

48. Warfarin _____

MATCH THE BRAND AND GENERIC NAMES

In the following exercises, match each brand name with its generic name. The Appendices on the Top 200 Brand Name Drugs, Top 200 Generic Drugs, and Top 200 Brand Name Drugs by Classification on pages 180-197 should be helpful. Answers are at the end of the book.

ANALGESICS

Brand Name	Generic Name
1. Tylenol w/Codeine _____	a. Tramadol
2. Ultram _____	b. Butalbital/APAP/Caffeine
3. Darvocet N-100 _____	c. Aspirin Enteric-Coated
4. Fioricet _____	d. Tramadol HCl/APAP
5. Ecotrin _____	e. Hydrocodone/APAP
6. Percocet _____	f. Oxycodone w/APAP
7. Ultracet _____	g. Propoxyphene-N/APAP
8. Vicodin _____	h. Acetaminophen w/Codeine

ANTI-INFECTIVES

Brand Name	Generic Name
1. Bactrim _____	a. Azithromycin
2. Augmentin _____	b. Cephalexin
3. Keflex _____	c. Amoxicillin/Potassium Clavulanate
4. Vibramycin _____	d. Trimethoprim/Sulfamethoxazole
5. Cleocin _____	e. Metronidazole
6. Zithromax _____	f. Clarithromycin
7. Flagyl _____	g. Clindamycin
8. Biaxin _____	h. Doxycycline

CARDIOVASCULAR AGENTS

Brand Name	Generic Name
1. Betapace _____	a. Sotalol
2. Zocor _____	b. Carvedilol
3. Pravachol _____	c. Warfarin
4. Coreg _____	d. Lovastatin

CARDIOVASCULAR AGENTS (cont'd)

Brand Name	Generic Name
5. Vasotec _____	e. Simvastatin
6. Mevacor _____	f. Pravastatin
7. Coumadin _____	g. Gemfibrozil
8. Lopid _____	h. Enalapril

DERMATOLOGICALS

Brand Name	Generic Name
1. Elocon _____	a. Clotrimazole/Betamethasone
2. Mycostatin _____	b. Mupirocin
3. Hytone _____	c. Clobetasol
4. Lotrisone _____	d. Ketoconazole
5. Temovate _____	e. Fluocinonide
6. Bactroban _____	f. Mometasone
7. Nizoral _____	g. Hydrocortisone
8. Lidex _____	h. Nystatin

GASTROINTESTINAL AGENTS

Brand Name	Generic Name
1. Zantac _____	a. Dicyclomine
2. Protonix _____	b. Omeprazole
3. Compazine _____	c. Ranitidine
4. Bentyl _____	d. Pantoprazole
5. Pepcid _____	e. Famotidine
6. Zofran _____	f. Diphenoxylate w/Atropine
7. Lomotil _____	g. Prochlorperazine
8. Prilosec _____	h. Ondansetron

MATCH THE BRAND AND GENERIC NAMES (cont'd)

Answers are at the end of the book.

HORMONES & MODIFIERS: ADRENAL CORTICOSTEROIDS

Brand Name	Generic Name
1. Deltasone _____	a. Prednisone
2. Medrol _____	b. Methylprednisolone
3. Prelone _____	c. Prednisolone
4. Decadron _____	d. Dexamethasone

HORMONES & MODIFIERS: ORAL ANTIDIABETICS

Brand Name	Generic Name
1. Glucovance _____	a. Metformin
2. Micronase _____	b. Glimepiride
3. Amaryl _____	c. Glyburide
4. Glucotrol _____	d. Glipizide
5. Glucophage _____	e. Glyburide/Metformin HCl

MUSCULOSKELETAL AGENTS

Brand Name	Generic Name
1. Flexeril _____	a. Allopurinol
2. Soma _____	b. Cyclobenzaprine
3. Fosamax _____	c. Carisoprodol
4. Zanaflex _____	d. Tizanidine
5. Robaxin _____	e. Methocarbamol
6. Zyloprim _____	f. Alendronate

NEUROLOGICAL AGENTS

Brand Name	Generic Name
1. Dilantin _____	a. Amphetamine Salt Combination
2. Requip _____	b. Methylphenidate
3. Concerta _____	c. Benztropine
4. Cogentin _____	d. Carbidopa/Levodopa
5. Adderall _____	e. Ropinirole

NEUROLOGICAL AGENTS (cont'd)

Brand Name	Generic Name
6. Tegretol _____	f. Gabapentin
7. Sinemet _____	g. Phenytoin
8. Neurontin _____	h. Carbamazepine

PSYCHOTROPIC AGENTS

Brand Name	Generic Name
1. Xanax _____	a. Alprazolam
2. Zoloft _____	b. Lorazepam
3. Buspar _____	c. Clonazepam
4. Prozac _____	d. Diazepam
5. Ativan _____	e. Buspirone
6. Celexa _____	f. Sertraline
7. Valium _____	g. Fluoxetine
8. Klonopin _____	h. Citalopram

RESPIRATORY AGENTS

Brand Name	Generic Name
1. Allegra _____	a. Fluticasone
2. Atarax _____	b. Fexofenadine
3. Tessalon _____	c. Promethazine
4. Vistaril _____	d. Hydroxyzine HCl
5. Phenergan _____	e. Hydroxyzine Pamoate
6. Ventolin _____	f. Benzonatate
7. Flonase _____	g. Albuterol

TRUE/FALSE

Indicate whether the statement is true or false in the blank. Answers are at the end of the book.

_____ 1. Once a suggested nonproprietary name for a drug is officially approved, it becomes the generic name of the drug.

_____ 2. Acetaminophen is an example of a salicylate.

_____ 3. Medullary paralysis is associated with an overdose of analgesic.

_____ 4. Ringworm is a type of fungal infection.

_____ 5. Vasopressors are used to treat hypertension.

_____ 6. Loperamide is a drug used to treat diarrhea.

_____ 7. Hematopoietic drugs are used to treat excessive bleeding.

_____ 8. Insulin is a cure for diabetes.

_____ 9. Calcium channel blockers are sometimes used to prevent migraine headaches.

_____ 10. Meprobamate is a barbiturate.

EXPLAIN WHY

Explain why these statements are true or important. Check your answers in the text. Discuss any questions you may have with your Instructor.

1. Why would an antibiotic not be appropriate for treating viral infections?

2. Why is it important for pharmacy technicians to be careful when handling antineoplastic drugs?

3. Why is it important for patients with diabetes to use a glucometer?

CHOOSE THE BEST ANSWER

Answers are at the end of the book.

1. The _____ designates nonproprietary names for drugs.
   a. manufacturer
   b. FDA
   c. USAN
   d. DEA

2. _____ is a neurotransmitter.
   a. Estrogen
   b. Testosterone
   c. Insulin
   d. Epinephrine

3. A common naturally occurring opiate-type drug is
   a. codeine.
   b. cocaine.
   c. meperidine.
   d. propoxyphene.

4. An inhalation anesthetic is
   a. propofol.
   b. isoflurane.
   c. etomidate.
   d. methohexital.

5. An antifungal drug is
   a. metronidazole.
   b. nystatin.
   c. indinavir.
   d. tetracycline.

6. The term used to denote the presence of a life-threatening cancerous group of cells or tumor is
   a. malignant.
   b. remission.
   c. benign.
   d. viral.

7. Drugs that decrease blood pressure by decreasing blood volume are called
   a. beta blockers.
   b. calcium channel blockers.
   c. diuretics.
   d. vasodilators.

8. Drugs that act to increase blood pressure are
   a. vasodilators.
   b. antihypertensives.
   c. vasopressors.
   d. ACE inhibitors.

9. Non-malignant skin growths are
   a. basal cells.
   b. keratoses.
   c. squamous cells.
   d. melanoma.

10. The histamine receptor antagonist with the most drug interactions is
    a. ranitidine.
    b. cimetidine.
    c. famotidine.
    d. nizatidine.

11. A commonly ordered stool softener is
    a. docusate sodium.
    b. lactulose.
    c. bismuth subsalicylate.
    d. loperamide.

12. _____ is used for vitamin B12 deficiency.
    a. Vitamin K
    b. Cyanocobalamin
    c. Ferrous sulfate
    d. Plasminogen

13. An adrenal cortex corticosteroid is
    a. hydrocortisone.
    b. thyroid.
    c. insulin.
    d. glucagon.

14. A drug that reduces uric acid and is used to treat gout is
    a. celecoxib.
    b. ibuprofen.
    c. allopurinol.
    d. cyclobenzaprine.

15. A drug commonly used to treat epilepsy is
    a. phenobarbital.
    b. sumatriptan.
    c. tacrine.
    d. donepezil.

TOP 200 BRAND NAME DRUGS

Following is a list of the Top 200 Brand Name Drugs cross-referenced with corresponding generic drug names and classifications. Rankings are based on Drug Topic's 2008 Top 200 list (available at http://drugtopics.modernmedicine.com/Pharmacy+Facts+&+Figures).

	Brand Name	Generic Name	Classification
1.	Lipitor	atorvastatin	Cardiovascular, Antihyperlipidemic
2.	Nexium	esomeprazole	Gastrointestinal, Antacid/Antiulcer
3.	Lexapro	escitalopram	Psychotropic, Antidepressant
4.	Singulair	montelukast	Respiratory
5.	Plavix	clopidogrel	Cardiovascular
6.	Synthroid	levothyroxine	Hormones & Modifiers, Thyroid
7.	Prevacid	lansoprazole	Gastrointestinal, Antacid/Antiulcer
8.	Advair Diskus	fluticasone and salmeterol	Respiratory
9.	Effexor XR	venlafaxine	Psychotropic, Antidepressant
10.	Diovan	valsartan	Cardiovascular, Antihypertensive*
11.	Crestor	rosuvastatin	Cardiovascular, Antihyperlipidemic
12.	Vytorin	ezetimibe and simvastatin	Cardiovascular, Antihyperlipidemic
13.	Cymbalta	duloxetine	Psychotropic
14.	ProAir HFA	albuterol	Respiratory, Bronchodilator
15.	Klor-Con	potassium chloride	Electrolyte
16.	Diovan HCT	hydrochlorothiazide and valsartan	Cardiovascular, Antihypertensive*
17.	Levaquin	levofloxacin	Anti-infective
18.	Actos	pioglitazone	Hormones & Modifiers, Oral antidiabetic
19.	Flomax	tamsulosin	Urinary
20.	Seroquel	quetiapine	Psychotropic, Antipsychotic
21.	Zetia	ezetimibe	Cardiovascular, Antihyperlipidemic
22.	Tricor	fenofibrate	Cardiovascular, Antihyperlipidemic
23.	Celebrex	celecoxib	Analgesic, NSAID
24.	Nasonex	mometasone	Respiratory
25.	Premarin Tablets	conjugated estrogens	Hormones & Modifiers, Estrogen
26.	Lantus	insulin glargine	Hormones & Modifiers, Insulin
27.	Viagra	sildenafil	Hormones & Modifiers, Phosphodiesterase inhibitor
28.	Yaz	drosperinone and ethinyl estradiol	Hormones and Modifiers, Contraceptive
29.	Lyrica	pregabalin	Neurological
30.	Adderall XR	dextroamphetamine and amphetamine	Psychotropic/Neurologic/AD(H)D
31.	Valtrex	valacyclovir	Anti-infective, Antiviral

*An asterisk next to a drug's classification indicates there are additional common uses for that drug.

Brand Name	Generic Name	Classification
32. Cozaar	losartan	Cardiovascular, Antihypertensive*
33. Topamax	topiramate	Neurological
34. Concerta	methylphenidate	Psychotropic/Neurologic/AD(H)D
35. Levoxyl	levothyroxine	Hormones & Modifiers, Thyroid
36. Actonel	risedronate	Musculoskeletal, Osteoporitic
37. Ambien CR	zolpidem	Psychotropic, Hypnotic
38. Spiriva	tiotropium	Respiratory
39. Benicar	olmesartan	Cardiovascular, Antihypertensive*
40. Xalatan	latanoprost	Ophthalmic, Antiglaucoma
41. Benicar HCT	olmesartan and hydrochlorothiazide	Cardiovascular, Antihypertensive*
42. Aricept	donepezil	Neurological, Anti-Alzheimer's
43. Ortho Tri Cyclen	norgestimate and ethinyl estradiol	Hormones & Modifiers, Contraceptive
44. Hyzaar	losartan and hydrochlorothiazide	Cardiovascular, Antihypertensive*
45. Tri-Sprintec	norgestimate and ethinyl estradiol	Hormones & Modifiers, Contraceptive
46. Cialis	tadalafil	Hormones and Modifiers, Phosphodiesterase inhibitor
47. OxyContin	oxycodone	Analgesic, Opiate
48. Aciphex	rabeprazole	Gastrointestinal, Antacid/Antiulcer
49. Lunesta	eszopiclone	Psychotropic, Hypnotic
50. Lamictal	lamotrigine	Neurological, Antiepileptic*
51. Detrol LA	tolterodine	Urinary
52. Chantix	varenicline	Psychotropic, Drug dependency
53. Avapro	irbesartan	Cardiovascular, Antihypertensive*
54. Proventil HFA	albuterol	Respiratory, Bronchodilator
55. Abilify	aripiprazole	Psychotropic, Antipsychotic
56. Yasmin 28	drospirenone and ethinyl estradiol	Hormones & Modifiers, Contraceptive
57. Budeprion XL	bupropion	Psychotropic
58. Niaspan	niacin	Cardiovascular, Antihyperlipidemic
59. Combivent	ipratropium and albuterol	Respiratory
60. Januvia	sitagliptin	Hormones & Modifiers, Oral antidiabetic
61. Boniva	ibandronate	Musculoskeletal, Osteoporitic
62. Trinessa	norgestimate and ethinyl estradiol	Hormones & Modifiers, Contraceptive
63. NuvaRing	etonogestrel and ethinyl estradiol	Hormones & Modifiers, Contraceptive
64. Risperdal	risperidone	Psychotropic, Antipsychotic
65. Polymagma Plain	attapulgite	Gastrointestinal, Antidiarrheal

TOP 200 BRAND NAME DRUGS

Brand Name	Generic Name	Classification
66. Flovent HFA	fluticasone	Respiratory
67. Imitrex Oral	sumatriptan	Neurological, Antimigraine
68. Evista	raloxifene	Musculoskeletal, Osteoporitic
69. Avelox	moxifloxacin	Anti-infective
70. Depakote ER	divalproex sodium	Neurological
71. Protonix	pantoprazole	Gastrointestinal, Antacid/Antiulcer
72. Avalide	irbesartan and hydrochlorothiazide	Cardiovascular, Antihypertensive*
73. Lidoderm	lidocaine transdermal	Anesthetic, Local
74. Zyprexa	olanzapine	Psychotropic, Antipsychotic
75. Namenda	memantine	Neurological, Anti-Alzheimer's
76. Tussionex	hydrocodone and chlorpheniramine	Respiratory
77. Thyroid, Armour	desiccated thyroid	Hormones & Modifiers, Thyroid
78. Humalog	insulin lispro	Hormones & Modifiers, Insulin
79. Vigamox	moxifloxacin ophthalmic	Ophthalmic
80. Tamiflu	oseltamivir	Anti-infective, Antiviral
81. Budeprion SR	bupropion	Psychotropic, Antidepressant
82. Suboxone	buprenorphine and naloxone	Psychotropic, Drug dependency
83. Lanoxin	digoxin	Cardiovascular, Antiarrhythmic
84. Loestrin 24 Fe	ethinyl estradiol and norethindrone and iron	Hormones and Modifiers, Contraceptive
85. Avodart	dutasteride	Urinary
86. Coumadin	warfarin	Cardiovascular, Anticoagulant
87. Wellbutrin XL	bupropion	Psychotropic, Antidepressant
88. Endocet	oxycodone and acetaminophen	Analgesic, Opiate
89. Skelaxin	metaxalone	Musculoskeletal, Muscle relaxant
90. Nasacort AQ	triamcinolone	Respiratory
91. Keppra	levetiracetam	Neurological, Antiepileptic
92. Allegra-D 12 Hour	fexofenadine and pseudoephedrine	Respiratory
93. Strattera	atomoxetine	Psychotropic
94. Lovaza	omega-3 fatty acid	Cardiovascular, Antihyperlipidemic
95. Avandia	rosiglitazone	Hormones & Modifiers, Oral antidiabetic
96. Ocella	drospirenone and ethinyl estradiol	Hormones & Modifiers, Contraceptive
97. Vyvanse	lisdexamfetamine	Psychotropic
98. Toprol XL	metoprolol	Cardiovascular, Antihypertensive*
99. Levitra	vardenafil	Hormones and Modifiers, Phosphodiesterase inhibitor

Brand Name	Generic Name	Classification
100. Astelin	azelastine	Respiratory, Antihistamine
101. Vivelle-DOT	estradiol	Hormones & Modifiers, Estrogen
102. Glipizide XL	glipizide	Hormones & Modifiers, Oral antidiabetic
103. Xopenex HFA	levalbuterol	Respiratory, Bronchodilator
104. Aviane	levonorgestrel and ethinyl estradiol	Hormones & Modifiers, Contraceptive
105. Fosamax	alendronate	Musculoskeletal, Osteoporitic
106. Kariva	desogestrel and ethinyl estradiol	Hormones & Modifiers, Contraceptive
107. Byetta	exenatide	Hormones & Modifiers
108. Mirapex	pramipexole	Neurological, Antiparkinsonian
109. Prempro	conjugated estrogens and medroxyprogesterone	Hormones & Modifiers
110. Low-Ogestrel	ethinyl estradiol and norgestrel	Hormones & Modifiers, Contraceptive
111. Patanol	olopatadine	Ophthalmic
112. Lumigan	bimatoprost	Ophthalmic, Antiglaucoma
113. Provigil	modafinil	Psychotropic
114. Pulmicort Respules	budesonide	Respiratory
115. Altace	ramipril	Cardiovascular, Antihypertensive*
116. Necon 1/35	norethindrone and ethinyl estradiol	Hormones & Modifiers, Contraceptive
117. Micardis	telmisartan	Cardiovascular, Antihypertensive*
118. Depakote	divalproex sodium	Neurological
119. Fosamax Plus D	alendronate sodium and cholecalciferol	Musculoskeletal, Osteoporitic
120. Alphagan P	brimonidine	Ophthalmic, Antiglaucoma
121. Geodon Oral	ziprasidone	Psychotropic, Antipsychotic
122. Micardis HCT	telmisartan and hydrochlorothiazide	Cardiovascular, Antihypertensive*
123. Vesicare	solifenacin	Urinary
124. Focalin XR	dexmethylphenidate	Psychotropic/Neurologic/AD(H)D
125. Digitek	digoxin	Cardiovascular, Antiarrhythmic
126. Sprintec	norgestimate and ethinyl estradiol	Hormones & Modifiers, Contraceptive
127. Xopenex	levalbuterol	Respiratory, Bronchodilator
128. Tobradex	tobramycin and dexamethasone	Ophthalmic
129. Humulin N	insulin (human recombinant)	Hormones & Modifiers, Insulin
130. Clarinex	desloratadine	Respiratory, Antihistamine
131. Ciprodex Otic	ciprofloxacin and dexamethasone	Otic
132. Coreg CR	carvedilol	Cardiovascular, Antihypertensive*
133. Apri	desogestrel and ethinyl estradiol	Hormones & Modifiers, Contraceptive
134. Atacand	candesartan	Cardiovascular, Antihypertensive*

TOP 200 BRAND NAME DRUGS

Brand Name	Generic Name	Classification
135. Levothroid	levothyroxine	Hormones & Modifiers, Thyroid
136. Restasis	cyclosporine	Ophthalmic
137. Ventolin HFA	albuterol	Respiratory, Bronchodilator
138. Rhinocort Aqua	budesonide	Respiratory
139. Prometrium	progesterone	Hormones & Modifiers, Progestin
140. Trivora-28	levonorgestrel and ethinyl estradiol	Hormones & Modifiers, Contraceptive
141. Xyzal	levocetirizine	Respiratory, Antihistamine
142. Ortho Evra	norelgestromin and ethinyl estradiol	Hormones and Modifiers, Contraceptive
143. Cosopt	dorzolamide and timolol	Ophthalmic, Antiglaucoma
144. Arimidex	anastrozole	Antineoplastic, Hormone
145. Veramyst	fluticasone	Respiratory
146. Requip	ropinirole	Neurological, Antiparkinsonian
147. Humulin 70/30	insulin (human recombinant)	Hormones & Modifiers, Insulin
148. BenzaClin	clindamycin and benzoyl peroxide	Dermatological
149. Differin	adapalene	Dermatological
150. Methylin	methylphenidate	Psychotropic/Neurologic/AD(H)D
151. Asacol	mesalamine	Gastrointestinal
152. Dilantin	phenytoin	Neurological, Anti-epileptic
153. Zymar	gatifloxacin	Ophthalmic
154. Vagifem	estrogen	Hormones & Modifiers, Estrogen
155. AndroGel	testosterone	Hormones & Modifiers, Androgen
156. Ethedent	sodium fluoride	Dental
157. Lantus SoloSTAR	insulin glargine [rDNA origin]	Hormones & Modifiers, Insulin
158. Fluvirin	influenza vaccine, inactivated	Immunobiologic, Vaccine
159. Premarin Vaginal	conjugated estrogens	Hormones & Modifiers, Estrogen
160. Actoplus Met	metformin and pioglitazone	Hormones & Modifiers, Oral antidiabetic
161. Propecia	finasteride	Hormones & Modifiers
162. NovoLog Mix 70/30	insulin aspart protamine and insulin aspart (rDNA origin)	Hormones & Modifiers, Insulin
163. Asmanex	mometasone	Respiratory
164. Levora	levonorgestrel and ethinyl estradiol	Hormones & Modifiers, Contraceptive
165. Uroxatral	alfuzosin	Urinary
166. Allegra-D 24	fexofenadine and pseudoephedrine	Respiratory
167. Epipen	epinephrine	Respiratory
168. Zyrtec	cetirizine	Respiratory, Antihistamine
169. Enablex	darifenacin	Urinary

Brand Name	Generic Name	Classification
170. Levemir	insulin detemir (rDNAorigin)	Hormones & Modifiers, Insulin
171. Fluzone	influenza vaccine, inactivated	Immunobiologic, Vaccine
172. Relpax	eletriptan	Neurological, Antimigraine
173. Symbicort	formoterol and budesonide	Respiratory
174. Janumet	metformin and sitagliptin	Hormones & Modifiers, Oral antidiabetic
175. Pataday	olopatadine	Ophthalmic
176. Travatan	travoprost	Ophthalmic, Antiglaucoma
177. Halflytely Bowel Prep Kit	PEG-3350, sodium chloride, sodium bicarbonate and potassium chloride for oral solution and bisacodyl	Gastrointestinal, Laxative
178. Travatan Z	travoprost	Ophthalmic, Antiglaucoma
179. Primacare One	prenatal multivitamins with folic acid	Hematological
180. Bactroban	mupirocin	Dermatological
181. C-Phen DM	chlorpheniramine, dextromethorphan and phenylephrine	Respiratory
182. Trilyte	PEG-3350, sodium chloride, sodium bicarbonate and potassium chloride	Gastrointestinal, Laxative
183. Welchol	colesevelam	Cardiovascular, Antihyperlipidemic
184. Lovenox	enoxaparin	Cardiovascular, Anticoagulant
185. Junel FE	norethindrone acetate, ethinyl estradiol and ferrous fumarate	Hormones & Modifiers, Contraceptive
186. Novolin 70/30	human insulin isophane suspension and regular, human insulin injection (rDNA origin)	Hormones & Modifiers, Insulin
187. Sular	nisoldipine	Cardiovascular, Antihypertensive*
188. Ultram ER	tramadol	Analgesic
189. Zovirax Topical	acyclovir	Dermatological
190. Catapres-TTS	clonidine	Cardiovascular, Antihypertensive*
191. Avandamet	rosiglitazone and metformin	Hormones & Modifiers, Oral antidiabetic
192. Maxalt	rizatriptan	Neurological, Anti-migraine
193. Jantoven	warfarin	Cardiovascular, Anticoagulant
194. Paxil CR	paroxetine	Psychotropic, Antidepressant
195. Femara	letrozole	Antineoplastic, Hormone
196. Aldara	imiquimod	Dermatological
197. Cytomel	liothyronine	Hormones & Modifiers, Thyroid
198. Cryselle	ethinyl estradiol and norgestrel	Hormones & Modifiers, Contraceptive
199. CellCept	mycophenolate	Hormones & Modifiers
200. QVAR	beclomethasone	Respiratory

TOP 200 GENERIC DRUGS

Following is a list of the Top 200 Generic Drugs cross-referenced with corresponding brand name(s) and classifications. Rankings are based on Drug Topic's 2008 Top 200 Generic Drugs by Pre-scriptions list (available at http://drugtopics.modernmedicine.com/Phar-macy+Facts+&+Figures).

	Generic Name	Brand Name	Classification
1.	Hydrocodone/APAP	Vicodin	Analgesic, Opiate
2.	Lisinopril	Zestril, Prinivil	Cardiovascular, Antihypertensive*
3.	Simvastatin	Zocor	Cardiovascular, Antihyperlipidemic
4.	Levothyroxine	Synthroid	Hormones & Modifiers, Thyroid
5.	Amoxicillin	Trimox	Anti-infective
6.	Azithromycin	Zithromax	Anti-infective
7.	Hydrochlorothiazide	Hydrodiuril	Cardiovascular, Antihypertensive*
8.	Alprazolam	Xanax	Psychotropic
9.	Atenolol	Tenormin	Cardiovascular, Antihypertensive*
10.	Metformin	Glucophage	Hormones & Modifiers, Oral antidiabetic
11.	Metoprolol Succinate	Toprol	Cardiovascular, Antihypertensive*
12.	Furosemide Oral	Lasix	Cardiovascular, Antihypertensive*
13.	Metoprolol Tartrate	Lopressor	Cardiovascular, Antihypertensive*
14.	Sertraline	Zoloft	Psychotropic, Antidepressant
15.	Omeprazole	Prilosec	Gastrointestinal, Antacid/Antiulcer
16.	Zolpidem Tartrate	Ambien	Psychotropic, Hypnotic
17.	Oxycodone w/APAP	Percocet	Analgesic, Opiate
18.	Ibuprofen	Motrin	Analgesic, NSAID
19.	Prednisone Oral	Deltasone	Hormones & Modifiers, Adrenal corticosteroid
20.	Fluoxetine	Prozac	Psychotropic, Antidepressant
21.	Warfarin	Coumadin	Cardiovascular, Anticoagulant
22.	Cephalexin	Keflex	Anti-infective
23.	Lorazepam	Ativan	Psychotropic
24.	Clonazepam	Klonopin	Psychotropic
25.	Citalopram HBr	Celexa	Psychotropic, Antidepressant
26.	Tramadol	Ultram	Analgesic
27.	Gabapentin	Neurontin	Neurological, Anti-epileptic
28.	Ciprofloxacin HCl	Cipro	Anti-infective
29.	Propoxyphene-N/APAP	Darvocet N-100	Analgesic, Opiate
30.	Lisinopril/HCTZ	Prinizide, Zestoretic	Cardiovascular, Antihypertensive*
31.	Triamterene w/HCTZ	Dyazide, Maxzide	Cardiovascular, Antihypertensive*

*An asterisk next to a drug's classification indicates there are additional common uses for that drug.

Generic Name	Brand Name	Classification
32. Amoxicillin/Potassium Clavulanate	Augmentin	Anti-infective
33. Cyclobenzaprine	Flexeril	Musculoskeletal, Muscle relaxant
34. Trazodone HCl	Desyrel	Psychotropic, Antidepressant
35. Fexofenadine	Allegra	Respiratory, Antihistamine
36. Fluticasone Nasal	Flonase	Respiratory
37. Paroxetine	Paxil	Psychotropic, Antidepressant
38. Lovastatin	Mevacor	Cardiovascular, Antihyperlipidemic
39. Trimethoprim/Sulfamethoxazole	Bactrim, Septra	Anti-infective
40. Albuterol Aerosol	Ventolin, Proventil, AccuNeb, Vospire, ProAir	Respiratory, Bronchodilator
41. Diazepam	Valium	Psychotropic
42. Pravastatin	Pravachol	Cardiovascular, Antihyperlipidemic
43. Acetaminophen w/Codeine	Tylenol w/Codeine	Analgesic, Opiate
44. Alendronate	Fosamax	Musculoskeletal, Osteoporitic
45. Amitriptyline	Elavil	Psychotropic, Antidepressant
46. Naproxen	Naprosyn	Analgesic, NSAID
47. Fluconazole	Diflucan	Anti-infective, Antifungal
48. Enalapril	Vasotec	Cardiovascular, Antihypertensive*
49. Carvedilol	Coreg	Cardiovascular
50. Ranitidine HCl	Zantac	Gastrointestinal, Antacid/Antiulcer
51. Doxycycline	Vibramycin	Anti-infective
52. Carisoprodol	Soma	Musculoskeletal, Muscle relaxant
53. Allopurinol	Zyloprim	Musculoskeletal, Antigout
54. Methylprednisolone	Medrol	Hormones & Modifiers, Adrenal corticosteroid
55. Meloxicam	Mobic	Analgesic, NSAID
56. Amlodipine Besylate/Benazepril	Lotrel	Cardiovascular, Antihypertensive*
57. Potassium Chloride	K-Dur, K-Lor, K-Tab, Kaon CL, Klorvess, Slow-K, Ten-K, Klotrix, K-Lyte CL	Electrolyte
58. Clonidine	Catapres	Cardiovascular, Antihypertensive*
59. Promethazine	Phenergan	Respiratory, Antihistamine
60. Isosorbide Mononitrate	Imdur, Ismo, Monoket	Cardiovascular
61. Folic Acid	Folvite	Hematological, Hematopoietic
62. Spironolactone	Aldactone	Cardiovascular, Antihypertensive*
63. Glimepiride	Amaryl	Hormones & Modifiers, Oral antidiabetic
64. Pantoprazole	Protonix	Gastrointestinal, Antacid/Antiulcer

187

TOP 200 GENERIC DRUGS

Generic Name	Brand Name	Classification
65. Glyburide	Micronase, Diabeta, Glynase Prestab	Hormones & Modifiers, Oral antidiabetic
66. Verapamil SR	Calan SR, Isoptin SR	Cardiovascular, Antihypertensive*
67. Albuterol Nebulizer Solution	Proventil, Ventolin	Respiratory, Bronchodilator
68. Cefdinir	Omnicef	Anti-infective
69. Temazepam	Restoril	Psychotropic, Hypnotic
70. Triamcinolone Acetenoide Topical	Kenalog, Aristocort	Dermatological
71. Penicillin VK	Pen Vee K	Anti-infective
72. Oxycodone	Oxycontin	Analgesic, Opiate
73. Metformin HCl ER	Glucophage XR	Hormones & Modifiers, Oral antidiabetic
74. Benazepril	Lotensin	Cardiovascular, Antihypertensive*
75. Glipizide	Glucotrol	Hormones & Modifiers, Oral antidiabetic
76. Clindamycin	Cleocin	Anti-infective
77. Ramipril	Altace	Cardiovascular, Antihypertensive*
78. Metronidazole	Flagyl	Anti-infective
79. Digoxin	Lanoxin, Digitek	Cardiovascular, Antiarrhythmic
80. Metoclopramide	Reglan	Gastrointestinal
81. Estradiol Oral	Estrace	Hormones & Modifiers, Estrogen
82. Hydroxyzine HCl	Atarax	Respiratory, Antihistamine
83. Amphetamine Salt Combination	Adderall	Psychotropic/Neurologic/AD(H)D
84. Diclofenac Sodium SR	Voltaren SR	Analgesic, NSAID
85. Gemfibrozil	Lopid	Cardiovascular, Antihyperlipidemic
86. Propranolol	Inderal	Cardiovascular, Antihypertensive*
87. Vitamin D	Vitamin D	Vitamin
88. Quinapril	Accupril	Cardiovascular, Antihypertensive*
89. Promethazine/Codeine	Phenergan with Codeine	Respiratory
90. Doxazosin	Cardura	Cardiovascular, Antihypertensive*
91. Mirtazapine	Remeron	Psychotropic, Antidepressant
92. Glipizide ER	Glucotrol XL	Hormones & Modifiers, Oral antidiabetic
93. Phentermine	Adipex-P, Fastin, Obenix, Oby-Trim	Gastrointestinal
94. Acyclovir	Zovirax	Anti-infective, Antiviral
95. Meclizine HCl	Antivert	Gastrointestinal, Antiemetic
96. Potassium Chloride ER	Klor-Con	Electrolyte
97. Nitrofurantoin Monohydrate Micronized	Macrobid	Anti-infective
98. Sulfamethoxazole/Trimethoprim	Bactrim, Septra	Anti-infective

Generic Name	Brand Name	Classification
99. Fentanyl Transdermal	Duragesic	Analgesic, Opiate
100. Buspirone HCl	Buspar	Psychotropic
101. Diltiazem	Cardizem	Cardiovascular, Antihypertensive*
102. Nifedipine ER	Adalat CC	Cardiovascular, Antihypertensive*
103. Glyburide/Metformin HCl	Glucovance	Hormones & Modifiers, Oral antidiabetic
104. Methotrexate	Rheumatrex, Trexall	Antineoplastic, Antimetabolite
105. Cheratussin AC	Robitussin AC	Respiratory
106. Clotrimazole/Betamethasone	Lotrisone	Dermatological
107. Mupirocin	Bactroban	Dermatological
108. Benzonatate	Tessalon	Respiratory, Antitussive
109. Methadone HCl (Non-Injectable)	Dolophine	Analgesic, Opiate
110. Butalbital/APAP/Caffeine	Fioricet, Esgic	Analgesic
111. Polyethylene Glycol	MiraLAX	Gastrointestinal, Laxative
112. Diltiazem CD	Cardizem CD	Cardiovascular, Antihypertensive*
113. Bisoprolol/HCTZ	Ziac	Cardiovascular, Antihypertensive*
114. Minocycline	Minocin	Anti-infective
115. Terazosin	Hytrin	Cardiovascular, Antihypertensive*
116. Nabumetone	Relafen	Analgesic, NSAID
117. Famotidine	Pepcid	Gastrointestinal, Antacid/Antiulcer
118. Tizanidine HCl	Zanaflex	Musculoskeletal, Muscle relaxant
119. Ferrous Sulfate	Feosol	Hematological, Hematopoietic
120. Methocarbamol	Robaxin	Musculoskeletal, Muscle relaxant
121. Finasteride	Proscar	Urinary
122. Phenytoin Sodium	Dilantin	Neurological, Anti-epileptic
123. Insulin Aspart	NovoLog	Hormones & Modifiers, Antidiabetic
124. Clobetasol	Temovate	Dermatological
125. Chlorhexidine Gluconate	Peridex, Periochip, Perichlor, Periogard	Dental
126. Clarithromycin	Biaxin	Anti-infective
127. Dicyclomine HCl	Bentyl	Gastrointestinal
128. Phenazopyridine HCl	Pyridium	Urinary
129. Colchicine	Colchicine	Musculoskeletal, Antigout
130. Atenolol/Chlorthalidone	Tenoretic	Cardiovascular, Antihypertensive*
131. Felodipine ER	Plendil	Cardiovascular, Antihypertensive*
132. Bupropion XL	Wellbutrin XL	Psychotropic, Antidepressant
133. Bupropion SR	Wellbutrin SR	Psychotropic, Antidepressant

TOP 200 GENERIC DRUGS

Generic Name	Brand Name	Classification
134. Hydroxychloroquine	Plaquenil	Anti-infective, Antimalarial
135. Aspirin Enteric-Coated	Ecotrin	Analgesic
136. Baclofen	Lioresal	Musculoskeletal, Muscle relaxant
137. Tramadol HCl/APAP	Ultracet	Analgesic
138. Ketoconazole Topical	Nizoral	Dermatological
139. Nortriptyline	Pamelor, Aventyl	Psychotropic, Antidepressant
140. Risperidone	Risperdal	Psychotropic, Antipsychotic
141. Cefuroxime	Ceftin	Anti-infective
142. Nystatin Topical	Mycostatin	Dermatological
143. Prednisolone Sd. Phs. Oral	Orapred, Pediapred, Prelone	Hormones & Modifiers, Adrenal corticosteroid
144. Nitroquick	Nitrostat	Cardiovascular, Antianginal
145. Hydroxyzine Pamoate	Vistaril	Respiratory, Antihistamine
146. Etodolac	Lodine	Analgesic, NSAID
147. Benztropine	Cogentin	Neurological
148. Nitroglycerin	Nitro-Bid	Cardiovascular, Antianginal
149. Phenobarbital	Luminal	Neurological, Anti-epileptic
150. Nystatin Systemic	Mycostatin	Anti-infective, Antifungal
151. Morphine Sulfate ER	MS Contin	Analgesic, Opiate
152. Fluocinonide	Lidex	Dermatological
153. Hydrocortisone Topical	Hytone	Dermatological
154. Oxybutynin Chloride	Ditropan	Urinary
155. Lamotrigine	Lamictal	Neurological, Anti-epileptic
156. Labetalol	Normodyne, Trandate	Cardiovascular, Antihypertensive*
157. Hydralazine	Apresoline	Cardiovascular, Antihypertensive*
158. Nitrofurantoin Macrocrystals	Macrodantin	Anti-infective
159. Amiodarone	Cordarone, Pacerone	Cardiovascular, Antiarrhythmic
160. Indomethacin	Indocin	Analgesic, NSAID
161. Carbidopa/Levodopa	Sinemet	Neurological, Antiparkinsonian
162. Clindamycin Topical	Cleocin T	Dermatological
163. Ondansetron	Zofran	Gastrointestinal, Antiemetic
164. Lithium Carbonate	Eskalith	Psychotropic
165. Fosinopril Sodium	Monopril	Cardiovascular, Antihypertensive*
166. Medroxyprogesterone	Provera	Hormones & Modifiers, Progestin
167. Hydrocodone/Ibuprofen	Vicoprofen	Analgesic, Opiate, NSAID
168. Ropinirole HCl	Requip	Neurological, Antiparkinsonian

Generic Name	Brand Name	Classification
169. Terbinafine HCl	Lamisil	Anti-infective, Antifungal
170. Bupropion ER	Zyban	Psychotropic, Drug dependency
171. Promethazine DM	Phen-Tuss DM, Phenergan w/Dextromethorphan	Respiratory, Antitussive, Antihistamine
172. Diltiazem SR	Cardizem SR	Cardiovascular, Antihypertensive*
173. Carbamazepine	Tegretol	Neurological, Anti-epileptic
174. Benazepril/HCTZ	Lotensin HCT	Cardiovascular, Antihypertensive*
175. Oxcarbazepine	Trileptal	Neurological, Anti-epileptic
176. Prednisone Intensol	Intensol	Hormones & Modifiers, Adrenal corticosteroid
177. Tetracycline	Sumycin	Anti-infective
178. Doxepin	Sinequan, Adapin	Psychotropic, Antidepressant
179. Dexamethasone	Decadron	Hormones & Modifiers, Adrenal corticosteroid
180. Prochlorperazine Maleate	Compazine	Gastrointestinal, Antiemetic
181. Venlafaxine	Effexor	Psychotropic, Antidepressant
182. Nystatin/Triamcinolone	Myco-Triacet II, Mycolog II	Dermatological
183. Mometasone Topical	Elocon	Dermatological
184. Oxybutynin ER	Ditropan XL	Urinary
185. Cyanocobalamin	Cobal, Cyanoject, Cyomin, Vibal	Hematological, Hematopoietic
186. Sotalol	Betapace	Cardiovascular, Antiarrhythmic
187. Erythromycin Ophthalmic	Ilotycin	Ophthalmic
188. Piroxicam	Feldene	Analgesic, NSAID
189. Oxycodone HCl ER	Oxycontin	Analgesic, Opiate
190. Hyoscyamine	Anaspaz, Cystospaz, Donnamar, Levsin	Gastrointestinal, Antispasmodic
191. Torsemide	Demadex	Cardiovascular, Antihypertensive*
192. Naproxen Sodium	Anaprox	Analgesic, NSAID
193. Nadolol	Corgard	Cardiovascular, Antihypertensive*
194. Hydromorphone HCl	Dilaudid	Analgesic, Opiate
195. Bumetanide	Bumex	Cardiovascular, Antihypertensive*
196. Methylphenidate	Concerta, Ritalin	Psychotropic/Neurologic/AD(H)D
197. Nifedical XL	Procardia XL	Cardiovascular, Antihypertensive*
198. Microgestin Fe 1/20	Loestrin Fe 1/20	Hormones & Modifiers, Contraceptive
199. Prednisolone Acetate Ophthalmic	Pred Mild, Pred Forte	Ophthalmic
200. Diphenoxylate w/Atropine	Lomotil	Gastrointestinal, Antidiarrheal

TOP 200 BRAND NAME DRUGS BY CLASSIFICATION

Following is a list of the Top 200 Brand Name Drugs organized by classification and cross-referenced with corresponding generic drug names. Drugs included are based on rankings in Drug Topic's 2008 Top 200 list at http://drugtopics.modernmedicine.com/Pharmacy+Facts+&+Figures.

Class/Type	Brand Name	Generic Name
Analgesics		
Analgesic	Ultram ER	tramadol
Analgesic, NSAID	Celebrex	celecoxib
Analgesic, Opiate	OxyContin	oxycodone
Analgesic, Opiate	Endocet	oxycodone and acetaminophen
Anesthetic Agents		
Local	Lidoderm	lidocaine transdermal
Anti-infectives		
Anti-infective	Levaquin	levofloxacin
Anti-infective	Avelox	moxifloxacin
Antiviral	Valtrex	valacyclovir
Antiviral	Tamiflu	oseltamivir
Cardiovascular Agents		
Antiarrhythmic	Lanoxin	digoxin
Antiarrhythmic	Digitek	digoxin
Anticoagulant	Coumadin	warfarin
Anticoagulant	Lovenox	enoxaparin
Anticoagulant	Jantoven	warfarin
Antihyperlipidemic	Lipitor	atorvastatin
Antihyperlipidemic	Crestor	rosuvastatin
Antihyperlipidemic	Vytorin	ezetimibe and simvastatin
Antihyperlipidemic	Zetia	ezetimibe
Antihyperlipidemic	Tricor	fenofibrate
Antihyperlipidemic	Niaspan	niacin
Antihyperlipidemic	Lovaza	omega-3 fatty acid
Antihyperlipidemic	Welchol	colesevelam
Antihypertensive*	Diovan	valsartan
Antihypertensive*	Diovan HCT	hydrochlorothiazide and valsartan
Antihypertensive*	Cozaar	losartan

An asterisk next to a drug's classification indicates there are additional common uses for that drug.

Class/Type	Brand Name	Generic Name
Antihypertensive*	Benicar	olmesartan
Antihypertensive*	Benicar HCT	olmesartan and hydrochlorothiazide
Antihypertensive*	Hyzaar	losartan and hydrochlorothiazide
Antihypertensive*	Avapro	irbesartan
Antihypertensive*	Avalide	irbesartan and hydrochlorothiazide
Antihypertensive*	Toprol XL	metoprolol
Antihypertensive*	Altace	ramipril
Antihypertensive*	Micardis	telmisartan
Antihypertensive*	Micardis HCT	telmisartan and hydrochlorothiazide
Antihypertensive*	Coreg CR	carvedilol
Antihypertensive*	Atacand	candesartan
Antihypertensive*	Sular	nisoldipine
Antihypertensive*	Catapres-TTS	clonidine

Dental

Dental	Ethedent	sodium fluoride

Dermatologicals

Dermatological	BenzaClin	clindamycin and benzoyl peroxide
Dermatological	Differin	adapalene
Dermatological	Bactroban	mupirocin
Dermatological	Zovirax Topical	acyclovir
Dermatological	Aldara	imiquimod

Electrolytic Agents

Electrolyte	Klor-Con	potassium chloride

Gastrointestinal & Urinary Tract Agents

Gastrointestinal	Asacol	mesalamine
Antacid/Antiulcer	Nexium	esomeprazole
Antacid/Antiulcer	Prevacid	lansoprazole
Antacid/Antiulcer	Aciphex	rabeprazole
Antacid/Antiulcer	Protonix	pantoprazole
Antidiarrheal	Polymagma Plain	attapulgite
Laxative	Halflytely Bowel	PEG-3350, sodium chloride, sodium Prep Kit bicarbonate, potassium chloride for oral solution, and bisacodyl
Laxative	Trilyte	PEG-3350, sodium chloride, sodium bicarbonate and potassium chloride
Urinary	Flomax	tamsulosin
Urinary	Detrol LA	tolterodine
Urinary	Avodart	dutasteride
Urinary	Vesicare	solifenacin
Urinary	Uroxatral	alfuzosin

TOP 200 BRAND NAME DRUGS BY CLASSIFICATION

Class/Type	Brand Name	Generic Name
Gastrointestinal & Urinary Tract Agents (cont'd)		
Urinary	Enablex	darifenacin
Hematological Agents		
Hematological	Primacare One	prenatal multivitamins with folic acid
Hormones & Modifiers		
Hormones & Modifiers	CellCept	mycophenolate
Hormones & Modifiers	Byetta	exenatide
Hormones & Modifiers	Prempro	conjugated estrogens and medroxyprogesterone
Hormones & Modifiers	Propecia	finasteride
Androgen	AndroGel	testosterone
Contraceptive	Cryselle	ethinyl estradiol and norgestrel
Contraceptive	Yaz	drosperinone and ethinyl estradiol
Contraceptive	Ortho Tri Cyclen	norgestimate and ethinyl estradiol
Contraceptive	Tri-Sprintec	norgestimate and ethinyl estradiol
Contraceptive	Yasmin 28	drospirenone and ethinyl estradiol
Contraceptive	Trinessa	norgestimate and ethinyl estradiol
Contraceptive	NuvaRing	etonogestrel and ethinyl estradiol
Contraceptive	Loestrin 24 Fe	ethinyl estradiol and norethindrone and iron
Contraceptive	Ocella	drospirenone and ethinyl estradiol
Contraceptive	Aviane	levonorgestrel and ethinyl estradiol
Contraceptive	Kariva	desogestrel and ethinyl estradiol
Contraceptive	Low-Ogestrel	ethinyl estradiol and norgestrel
Contraceptive	Necon 1/35	norethindrone and ethinyl estradiol
Contraceptive	Sprintec	norgestimate and ethinyl estradiol
Contraceptive	Apri	desogestrel and ethinyl estradiol
Contraceptive	Trivora-28	levonorgestrel and ethinyl estradiol
Contraceptive	Ortho Evra	norelgestromin and ethinyl estradiol
Contraceptive	Levora	levonorgestrel and ethinyl estradiol
Contraceptive	Junel FE	norethindrone acetate, ethinyl estradiol and ferrous fumarate
Estrogen	Premarin Tablets	conjugated estrogens
Estrogen	Vivelle-DOT	estradiol
Estrogen	Vagifem	estrogen
Estrogen	Premarin Vaginal	conjugated estrogens

Class/Type	Brand Name	Generic Name
Insulin	Lantus	insulin glargine
Insulin	Humalog	insulin lispro
Insulin	Humulin N	insulin (human recombinant)
Insulin	Humulin 70/30	insulin (human recombinant)
Insulin	Lantus SoloSTAR	insulin glargine [rDNA origin]
Insulin	NovoLog Mix 70/30	insulin aspart protamine and insulin aspart (rDNA origin)
Insulin	Levemir	insulin detemir (rDNAorigin)
Insulin	Novolin 70/30	human insulin isophane suspension and regular, human insulin injection (rDNA origin)
Oral antidiabetic	Avandamet	rosiglitazone and metformin
Oral antidiabetic	Actos	pioglitazone
Oral antidiabetic	Januvia	sitagliptin
Oral antidiabetic	Avandia	rosiglitazone
Oral antidiabetic	Glipizide XL	glipizide
Oral antidiabetic	Actoplus Met	metformin and pioglitazone
Oral antidiabetic	Janumet	metformin and sitagliptin
Phosphodiesterase inhibitor	Viagra	sildenafil
Phosphodiesterase inhibitor	Cialis	tadalafil
Phosphodiesterase inhibitor	Levitra	vardenafil
Progestin	Prometrium	progesterone
Thyroid	Thyroid, Armour	desiccated thyroid
Thyroid	Cytomel	liothyronine
Thyroid	Synthroid	levothyroxine
Thyroid	Levoxyl	levothyroxine
Thyroid	Levothroid	levothyroxine

Immunobiologic Agents

Vaccine	Fluvirin	influenza vaccine, inactivated
Vaccine	Fluzone	influenza vaccine, inactivated

Musculoskeletal Agents

Muscle relaxant	Skelaxin	metaxalone
Osteoporitic	Actonel	risedronate
Osteoporitic	Boniva	ibandronate
Osteoporitic	Evista	raloxifene
Osteoporitic	Fosamax	alendronate
Osteoporitic	Fosamax Plus D	alendronate sodium and cholecalciferol

Neurological Agents

Neurological	Lyrica	pregabalin
Neurological	Topamax	topiramate
Neurological	Depakote ER	divalproex sodium
Neurological	Depakote	divalproex sodium

TOP 200 BRAND NAME DRUGS BY CLASSIFICATION

Class/Type	Brand Name	Generic Name
Neurological Agents (cont'd)		
Anti-Alzheimer's	Aricept	donepezil
Anti-Alzheimer's	Namenda	memantine
Antiepileptic	Keppra	levetiracetam
Antiepileptic*	Dilantin	phenytoin
Antiepileptic*	Lamictal	lamotrigine
Antimigraine	Imitrex Oral	sumatriptan
Antimigraine	Relpax	eletriptan
Antimigraine	Maxalt	rizatriptan
Antiparkinsonian	Mirapex	pramipexole
Antiparkinsonian	Requip	ropinirole
Ophthalmic & Otic Agents		
Ophthalmic	Patanol	olopatadine
Ophthalmic	Tobradex	tobramycin and dexamethasone
Ophthalmic	Restasis	cyclosporine
Ophthalmic	Zymar	gatifloxacin
Ophthalmic	Pataday	olopatadine
Antiglaucoma	Xalatan	latanoprost
Antiglaucoma	Lumigan	bimatoprost
Antiglaucoma	Alphagan P	brimonidine
Antiglaucoma	Cosopt	dorzolamide and timolol
Antiglaucoma	Travatan	travoprost
Antiglaucoma	Travatan Z	travoprost
Otic	Ciprodex Otic	ciprofloxacin and dexamethasone
Psychotropic Agents		
Psychotropic	Cymbalta	duloxetine
Psychotropic	Budeprion XL	bupropion
Psychotropic	Strattera	atomoxetine
Psychotropic	Vyvanse	lisdexamfetamine
Psychotropic	Provigil	modafinil
Antidepressant	Lexapro	escitalopram
Antidepressant	Effexor XR	venlafaxine
Antidepressant	Budeprion SR	bupropion
Antidepressant	Wellbutrin XL	bupropion
Antidepressant	Paxil CR	paroxetine

Class/Type	Brand Name	Generic Name
Antipsychotic	Seroquel	quetiapine
Antipsychotic	Abilify	aripiprazole
Antipsychotic	Risperdal	risperidone
Antipsychotic	Zyprexa	olanzapine
Antipsychotic	Geodon Oral	ziprasidone
Drug dependency	Chantix	varenicline
Drug dependency	Suboxone	buprenorphine and naloxone
Hypnotic	Ambien CR	zolpidem
Hypnotic	Lunesta	eszopiclone
Psychotropic/Neurologic/AD(H)D	Adderall XR	dextroamphetamine and amphetamine
Psychotropic/Neurologic/AD(H)D	Concerta	methylphenidate
Psychotropic/Neurologic/AD(H)D	Focalin XR	dexmethylphenidate
Psychotropic/Neurologic/AD(H)D	Methylin	methylphenidate

Respiratory Agents

Class/Type	Brand Name	Generic Name
Respiratory	Singulair	montelukast
Respiratory	Advair Diskus	fluticasone and salmeterol
Respiratory	Nasonex	mometasone
Respiratory	Spiriva	tiotropium
Respiratory	Combivent	ipratropium and albuterol
Respiratory	Flovent HFA	fluticasone
Respiratory	Tussionex	hydrocodone and chlorpheniramine
Respiratory	Nasacort AQ	triamcinolone
Respiratory	Allegra-D 12 Hour	fexofenadine and pseudoephedrine
Respiratory	Pulmicort Respules	budesonide
Respiratory	Rhinocort Aqua	budesonide
Respiratory	Veramyst	fluticasone
Respiratory	Asmanex	mometasone
Respiratory	Allegra-D 24	fexofenadine and pseudoephedrine
Respiratory	Epipen	epinephrine
Respiratory	Symbicort	formoterol and budesonide
Respiratory	C-Phen DM	chlorpheniramine, dextromethorphan and phenylephrine
Respiratory	QVAR	beclomethasone
Antihistamine	Astelin	azelastine
Antihistamine	Clarinex	desloratadine
Antihistamine	Xyzal	levocetirizine
Antihistamine	Zyrtec	cetirizine
Bronchodilator	ProAir HFA	albuterol
Bronchodilator	Proventil HFA	albuterol
Bronchodilator	Xopenex HFA	levalbuterol
Bronchodilator	Xopenex	levalbuterol
Bronchodilator	Ventolin HFA	albuterol

COMMONLY REFRIGERATED DRUGS

Many products must be stored at refrigerated temperatures to ensure stability. Following is a list of commonly refrigerated drugs. As per the manufacturer's product information, some products need to be refrigerated immediately upon receipt from the manufacturer. Others may be stored at room temperature but will require refrigeration once reconstituted or when a diluent is added. A few drugs are stored in the refrigerator at the pharmacy but can be kept at room temperature when in use by the patient. For reconstituted products, the manufacturer will provide information as to how long the product is stable once reconstituted.

Brand Name & Dosage Form	Generic Name
ActHib vials	haemophilus b conjugate vaccine (tetanus toxoid conjugate)
Actimmune vials	interferon gamma-1b
Adacel vials	tetanus toxoid, reduced diphtheria toxoid, acellular pertussis vaccine adsorbed (Tdap) vaccine
Alcaine ophthalmic solution	proparacaine
Amoxil suspension	amoxicillin
Anectine vials	succinylcholine chloride
Aspirin Uniserts suppositories	aspirin
Atgam vials	lymphocyte immune globulin
Augmentin suspension	amoxicillin/clavulanic acid
Avonex syringes	interferon beta-1a
Azasite ophthalmic solution	azithromycin
BACiiM vials	bacitracin
Benzamycin gel	erythromycin/benzoyl peroxide
Bicillin syringes	penicillin G benzathine
Cardizem vials	diltiazem hydrochloride
Caverject vials	alprostadil
Ceftin suspension	cefuroxime axetil
Cefzil suspension	cefprozil
Cerebyx vials	fosphenytoin sodium
Cipro suspension	ciprofloxacin
Combipatch transdermal patch	estradiol/norethindrone
Copaxone	glatiramer acetate
DDAVP vials	desmopressin
Digibind vials	digoxin immune Fab
Enbrel syringes	etanercept
Engerix-B vials	hepatitis B vaccine
Epogen vials	epoetin alfa
Genotropin cartridges	somatropin
Havrix vials, syringes	hepatitis A vaccine

Brand Name & Dosage Form	Generic Name
Hemabate vial	carboprost tromethamine
Humalog vials, pens	insulin lispro
Humira syringes	adalimumab
Humulin R vials	regular insulin
Infergen vials	interferon alfacon-1
Kaletra solution, capsules	lopinavir/ritonavir
Lactinex tablets	lactobacillus acidophilus/bulgaricus
Lantus vials, pens	insulin glargine
Leukeran tablets	chlorambucil
Meruvax vials	rubella virus vaccine live
Methergine vials	methylergonovine maleate
Miacalcin nasal spray	calcitonin salmon
MMR II vials	measles, mumps, rubella virus vaccine live
Mycostatin pastilles	nystatin
Neupogen vials, syringes	filgrastim
Nimbex vials	cisatracurium besylate
Norditropin cartridges	somatropin
Norvir soft gels	ritonavir
Neulasta syringe	pegfilgrastim
Neurontin suspension	gabapentin
Pavulon	pancuronium bromide
Phenergan suppositories	promethazine
Pneumovax 23 vaccine	pneumococcal vaccine polyvalent
Premarin Secule vials	conjugated estrogens
RabAvert vial	rabies vaccine
Rapamune solution	sirolimus
Rebetron	ribavirin/interferon alfa-2b
Regranex gel	becaplermin
Risperdal Consta kits	risperidone
Sandostatin vials	octreotide acetate
Suprax suspension	cefixime
Survanta vials	beractant
Tamiflu suspension	oseltamivir phosphate
Thyrolar tablets	liotrix
Tracrium vials	atracurium besylate
Veetids suspension	penicillin V
VePesid capsules	etoposide
Vibramycin suspension	doxycycline
Viroptic ophthalmic solution	trifluridine
Xalatan ophthalmic solution	latanoprost
Zemuron vials	rocuronium bromide
Zithromax suspension	azithromycin

PHARMACY TECHNICIAN CERTIFICATION EXAM (PTCE)

PRACTICE EXAM

The following multiple choice questions are in the *choose the best answer format* of the national Pharmacy Technician Certification Examination (PTCE) offered by the Pharmacy Technician Certification Board (PTCB). There are four possible answers with only one answer being the most correct. Many of these questions can be answered through a careful review of this workbook. However, others require knowledge gained from practice as a technician. Answers for all questions can be found on page 228.

Since the time limit for taking the PTCE is two hours, you may want to test your ability to answer the questions under a time limit, or you may simply wish to time yourself to see how long it takes you. There are 90 questions here, the same number as on the exam. If you wish to have a similar experience, you can allow yourself two hours to answer these questions.

For more information on the Pharmacy Technician Certification Exam, see the preface of this Workbook.

Answers are on page 228.

1. The pharmacist has asked you to obtain a MedWatch Form 3500 so s/he can report
   a. an adverse event regarding a veterinary product.
   b. an adverse event regarding a drug.
   c. an adverse event regarding a vaccine.
   d. an adverse event regarding a prescribing error.

2. Medications for ophthalmic administration are usually available in
   a. sterile hypotonic drops or sterile ointment.
   b. sterile hypertonic drops or sterile ointment.
   c. hypotonic solution or hypotonic suspension.
   d. sterile isotonic drops or sterile ointment.

3. A Class _____ drug recall is the most serious.
   a. I
   b. II
   c. III
   d. IV

4. IV's prepared containing cytotoxic drugs are prepared in a(n)
   a. biological safety cabinet.
   b. laminar flow hood.
   c. dark room.
   d. outpatient satellite.

5. Nolvadex® or _____ is an anti-estrogen type medication that is often used in the treatment of breast cancer.
   a. albuterol
   b. tamoxifen
   c. phenytoin
   d. nifedipine

6. After mixing Benzamycin® gel, how should it be stored?
   a. at room temperature
   b. in the refrigerator
   c. in a kitchen cupboard
   d. in a bathroom cupboard

7. When using a Class A prescription balance, the least weighable quantity is
   a. 6 mg.
   b. 120 mg.
   c. 500 mg.
   d. the same as the sensitivity requirement.

8. The form number for ordering Schedule II drugs is
   a. DEA Form 121.
   b. DEA Form 200.
   c. DEA Form 222.
   d. DEA Form 240.

9. What is the infusion rate in ml/min if a 500 ml IV is administered over 8 hours?
   a. 1
   b. 4
   c. 8
   d. 60

10. How much cough syrup will a patient take in 24 hours if the dose is two teaspoonfuls every six hours?
    a. 20 ml
    b. 30 ml
    c. 40 ml
    d. 80 ml

11. The smallest gelatin capsule used for extemporaneous compounding is size
    a. 10.
    b. 8.
    c. 5.
    d. 000.

12. Coring can occur when
    a. the needle is longer than the ampule.
    b. the patient has an allergy to latex.
    c. the needle is not correctly removed from the vial.
    d. the needle is not correctly inserted into the vial.

Answers are on page 228.

13. Furosemide or Lasix® is used as
    a. an analgesic.
    b. an anti-inflammatory agent.
    c. a sedative.
    d. a diuretic.

14. The infusion rate of an IV is over 12 hours. The total exact volume is 800 ml. What would be the infusion rate in mls per minute?
    a. 0.56 ml/minute
    b. 1.11 ml/minute
    c. 2.7 ml/minute
    d. none of the above

15. You have a 70% solution of dextrose. How many grams of dextrose is in 400 ml of this solution?
    a. 700 grams
    b. 460 grams
    c. 280 grams
    d. 120 grams

16. The standard pediatric dose for cefazolin is 20 mg/kg/day. The order is written for 150 mg TID. The infant weighs 8 lb. This dose is
    a. too high.
    b. too low.
    c. within guidelines.

17. Federal law requires pharmacies to have available for inspection Copy 3 of the DEA Form 222 for a period of _____ year(s).
    a. 1
    b. 4
    c. 3
    d. 2

18. An IV order calls for the addition of 45 mEq of $CaCO_3$ (calcium carbonate). You have a 25 ml vial of $CaCO_3$ 4.4mEq/ml. How many ml of this concentrate do you need to add to this IV?
    a. 5.6 ml
    b. 8.4 ml
    c. 10.2 ml
    d. 12.8 ml

19. In this formula, how much talc is needed to fill 120 grams?
    Nupercainal® Ointment 4%
    zinc oxide 20%
    talc 2%
    a. 1200 mg
    b. 1500 mg
    c. 2000 mg
    d. 2400 mg

20. A bottle of nitroglycerin has the labeled strength of 1/200 grains. What would this strength be in milligrams?
    a. 0.2 mg
    b. 0.3 mg
    c. 0.4 mg
    d. 0.6 mg

21. A pharmacy wants to mark-up a product by thirty percent. How much would an item cost with this mark-up, if its original cost was $4.50?
    a. $5.85
    b. $6.23
    c. $6.40
    d. $7.10

22. Federal law requires an exact inventory must be kept for
    a. phenobarbital.
    b. alprazolam.
    c. carisoprodal.
    d. morphine sulfate.

23. The Material Safety Data Sheets (MSDS)
    a. provide protocols for fire hazards in the pharmacy setting.
    b. provide safety codes by OSHA in the storage of inventory.
    c. provide information concerning hazardous substances.
    d. none of the above

Answers are on page 228.

24. How much diluent do you need to add to 4 gm of powder to get a concentration of 500 mg/ml?
    a. 0.8 ml
    b. 8 ml
    c. 1.0 ml
    d. 10 ml

25. What does DAW mean on a written prescription?
    a. The medication ordered is a controlled substance.
    b. The medication should be taken with water.
    c. The brand name is to be dispensed as written.
    d. Refills are limited to six months.

26. Your pharmacy has received a prescription for Ointment XYZ and it is not available commercially. The prescription is written for 30 g with 2 refills. According to FDA guidelines, what is the largest amount your pharmacy can compound when originally filling the prescription in anticipation of refills?
    a. 90 g
    b. 120 g
    c. 30 g
    d. 60 g

27. The last set of digits of the NDC are indicative of
    a. the manufacturer.
    b. product identification.
    c. package size.
    d. none of the above.

28. The approximate size container for the dispensing of 180 ml of liquid medication would be?
    a. 2 ounces
    b. 4 ounces
    c. 6 ounces
    d. 8 ounces

29. A patient asks whether he/she can take a certain medication with another one? As a pharmacy technician what should you do?
    a. Inform the patient that you see no problem.
    b. Provide the patient with a drug insert.
    c. Request the patient see the pharmacist for a consult.
    d. Try to sell the patient some Mylanta®.

30. The doctor writes: ii gtts OU bid. What does this mean?
    a. two drops in the left eye twice a day
    b. two drops in the right eye twice a day
    c. two drops in each eye twice a day
    d. two drops in the right ear twice a day

31. Investigational drugs are regulated by the
    a. FDA.
    b. CMS.
    c. DEA.
    d. Board of Pharmacy.

32. Which of the following books is used for FDAs list of approved drug products?
    a. *Merck Index*
    b. *Red Book*
    c. "Orange Book"
    d. Martindale

33. Propranolol is the same as
    a. Inderal®.
    b. Tenormin®.
    c. lisinopril.
    d. Corgard®.

34. Thiazide diuretics are used to
    a. relieve migraine headaches.
    b. relieve gastroenteritis.
    c. manage pain.
    d. manage the retention of water.

PTCE PRACTICE EXAM

Answers are on page 228.

35. Of the following, which one deals with the issue of safety caps on prescription bottles?
    a. The Controlled Substance Act
    b. The Poison Prevention Act
    c. Hazardous Substance Act
    d. Federal Food and Cosmetic Act

36. Which form of insulin is a clear solution?
    a. Humulin R®
    b. Humulin N®
    c. Humulin L®
    d. Humulin 70/30®

37. The appearance of crystals in mannitol injection would indicate that the product
    a. was exposed to cold.
    b. has settled during shipment.
    c. contains impurities and should be returned.
    d. was formulated using sterile saline.

38. How many 30 mg $KMnO_4$ (Potassium Permanganate) tablets are needed to make the following solution? $KMnO_4$ 1:5000 600 ml
    a. 2 tablets
    b. 3 tablets
    c. 4 tablets
    d. 6 tablets

39. Dextrose 25% 1000 ml is ordered. You have only dextrose 70% solution available. How much of the dextrose 70% solution and sterile water will you use to fill this order?
    a. 250 ml dextrose 70% and 750 ml sterile water
    b. 357 ml dextrose 70% and 643 ml sterile water
    c. 424 ml dextrose 70% and 576 ml sterile water
    d. none of the above

40. The Occupational, Safety, Health Administration (OSHA) requires pharmacies to have Material Safety Data Sheets (MSDS) for
    a. all drugs in the pharmacy inventory.
    b. all materials stored in the pharmacy refrigerator.
    c. each hazardous chemical used in the pharmacy.
    d. all controlled substances in the pharmacy inventory.

41. Of the following group names, which one would be used for cough?
    a. anthelmintics
    b. antitussives
    c. antihistamines
    d. anticholinergics

42. Tobrex® ophthalmic ung refers to
    a. an ointment used for the eye.
    b. a solution used for the eye.
    c. a topical ointment for external use only.
    d. an ointment used for the ear.

43. Suspending or thickening agents are added to suspensions to thicken the suspending medium and the sedimentation rate. Which of the following is not a suspending agent?
    a. carboxymethylcellulose
    b. tragacanth
    c. acacia
    d. bentonite

44. Oral Polio Virus Vaccine (Poliovax®) should be stored in a temperature not to exceed 46 degrees Fahrenheit. What is this temperature in Centigrade?

    Use this formula: Centigrade = 5/9 (F° - 32°)
    a. 6°C
    b. 8°C
    c. 10°C
    d. 12°C

Answers are on page 228.

45. You receive a prescription for amoxicillin 75 mg QID for ten days. How many ml of amoxicillin 250 mg/5ml do you need to fill this prescription to last the full ten days?
    a. 20 ml
    b. 40 ml
    c. 60 ml
    d. 100 ml

46. The doctor writes for aminophylline 125 mg po QID x 10 days. You only have the solution 250 mg/5 ml. How much would be needed for one dose?
    a. 1/4 teaspoonful
    b. 1/2 teaspoonful
    c. 3/4 teaspoonful
    d. 1 1/2 teaspoonful

47. You receive a prescription for sertraline (Zoloft®) qd x 30 days. What is sertraline?
    a. antihypertensive
    b. anticonvulsant
    c. antidepressant
    d. antianginal

48. All aseptic manipulations in the laminar flow hood should be performed at least
    a. four inches within the hood.
    b. six inches within the hood.
    c. eight inches within the hood.
    d. twelve inches within the hood.

49. Which auxiliary label would be used for a prescription for tetracycline 250 mg capsules?
    a. May Cause Drowsiness
    b. Avoid Aspirin
    c. Avoid Dairy Products and Antacids
    d. Take with Food

50. You receive an order for Kaopectate® 30 ml bid prn. How many tablespoons is one dose equal to?
    a. 5 tablespoons
    b. 3 tablespoons
    c. 2 tablespoons
    d. 1 tablespoon

51. Which of the following is a Schedule II Controlled Substance?
    a. diazepam
    b. meperidine
    c. pentazocine
    d. propoxyphene

52. If the manufacturer's expiration date for a drug is 12/10, the drug is considered acceptable to dispense until which date?
    a. 12/01/10
    b. 12/31/10
    c. 11/30/10
    d. 1/01/10

53. The Roman numerals XLII is equivalent to
    a. 42.
    b. 62.
    c. 92.
    d. 402.

54. The laminar flow hood should be left operating continuously. If it is turned off, it should not be used until it has been running for at least
    a. ten minutes.
    b. thirty minutes.
    c. forty-five minutes.
    d. sixty minutes.

55. Which auxiliary label would you use for this particular sig: ii gtts AU bid?
    a. take with meals
    b. for the ear
    c. avoid sunlight
    d. for the eye

56. A dose is written for 5 mg/kg every eight hours for one day. The adult to take this medication weighs 145 pounds. How much drug will be needed to fill this order?
    a. 765 mg
    b. 844 mg
    c. 989 mg
    d. 1254 mg

Answers are at on page 228.

57. How much medication would be needed for the following order?

    prednisone 10 mg, one qid x 4 days, one tid x 2 days, one bid x 1 day, then stop
    a. 16
    b. 20
    c. 24
    d. 26

58. Benzethidine is in DEA Schedule I, meaning that benzethidine
    a. has a currently accepted medical use in the United States with severe restrictions.
    b. can only be handled by the pharmacist.
    c. has no currently accepted medical use in the world.
    d. has no currently accepted medical use in the United States.

59. In which controlled substance schedule is Tylenol® No. 2 classified?
    a. Schedule I
    b. Schedule II
    c. Schedule III
    d. Schedule IV

60. Assuming that one pint is equal to 473 ml, how many pints can be found in one liter?
    a. 1.5 pints
    b. 2.1 pints
    c. 2.8 pints
    d. 3.1 pints

61. The first line of defense against infection/ contamination of an IV product is
    a. antibiotics.
    b. antiseptics.
    c. disinfectants.
    d. handwashing.

62. HIPAA requires that
    a. all Medicaid patients are offered counseling by a pharmacist.
    b. all patients receive counseling by a pharmacist.
    c. all patients are offered counseling by a pharmacist.
    d. privacy rules are observed for PHI.

63. Which of the following medications must be administered in a glass IV container?
    a. aminophylline
    b. dopamine
    c. nitroglycerin
    d. potassium

64. The two parts of the syringe that should not be touched are
    a. the tip and needle.
    b. the collar and barrel.
    c. the tip and plunger.
    d. the collar and plunger.

65. The sale of what medication is restricted by the Combat Methamphetamine Epidemic Act (CMEA)?
    a. Claritin®
    b. Claritin-D 24®
    c. Chlor-Trimeton®
    d. Robitussin DM®

66. The first five digits of the National Drug Code (NDC) number identifies the
    a. product.
    b. manufacturer.
    c. units.
    d. type of packaging.

67. The "Orange Book" provides information about
    a. current pricing.
    b. drug product stability.
    c. generic equivalents.
    d. investigational drugs.

Answers are on page 228.

68. From the following directions how many tablets should be dispensed?

2 tabs po qid x 2 days, then 1 tab po tid x 2 days, then ss po bid x 2 days, then dc
a. 22
b. 23
c. 24
d. none of the above

69. What should the last digit be of this DEA number?

AB431762 ___
a. one
b. three
c. five
d. seven

70. Aminosyn® is an amino acid often used in TPN orders to provide protein for cellular repair and growth. A physician writes an order for Aminosyn® 2.5% 500 ml. You have only Aminosyn® 8.5% 500 ml. How do you prepare this order using a sterile evacuated container?
a. add 320 ml of Aminosyn® 8.5% and qs with sterile water to 500 ml
b. add 147 ml of Aminosyn® 8.5% and qs with sterile water to 500 ml
c. add 124 ml of Aminosyn® 8.5% and qs with sterile water to 500 ml
d. add 74 ml of Aminosyn® 8.5% and qs with sterile water to 500 ml

71. You are to use 2.4 ml of diluent to reconstitute a vial of medication. What size of syringe should be used?
a. 20 ml
b. 10 ml
c. 5 ml
d. 3 ml

72. Nitroglycerin is provided in a sublingual tablet. This means that the
a. tablet should be placed in the cheek.
b. tablet should be dissolved under the tongue.
c. tablet should be swallowed whole.
d. prescription must be dispensed in a glass bottle.

73. The type of formulary that allows the pharmacy to obtain all medications that are prescribed is a(an)
a. international formulary.
b. closed formulary.
c. wholesaler formulary.
d. open formulary.

74. Zantac®, Tagamet®, and Pepcid® are H2 blockers which are now available over-the-counter (OTC). What are these drugs used for?
a. used as an antihistamine to alleviate runny nose
b. used as an decongestant to unclog nasal passages
c. used to inhibit stomach acid secretion
d. used as an antacid in that it neutralizes stomach acid

75. A "hospital borne" infection is also known as a _____ infection.
a. nosocomial
b. infectious
c. superinfection
d. none of the above

76. Of the following drug recalls, which one is the most important in that all parties involved in the dispensing of a prescription (doctor, pharmacy, and patient) must be notified due to the drugs potential or serious harm?
a. Class I Recall
b. Classs II Recall
c. Class III Recall
d. Classs IV Recall

Answers are on page 228.

77. The pharmacist should be alerted if a patient is allergic to codeine and prescribed
    a. alprazolam.
    b. Robitussin AC®.
    c. methylphenidate.
    d. phenobarbital.

78. A prescription for amoxicillin 250 mg #30 has a usual and customary price of $8.49. The acquisition cost of amoxicillin 250 mg #30 is $2.02. What is the gross profit?
    a. $2.02
    b. $6.47
    c. 50%
    d. 1/3

79. A senior citizen is paying for a prescription for penicillin VK 250 mg #30. The usual and customary price is $8.49. However this patient qualifies for a 10% discount. How much will the patient pay?
    a. $8.49
    b. $6.99
    c. $8.39
    d. $7.64

80. A medication used to reduce a fever is called an
    a. antipyretic.
    b. antitussive.
    c. antiemetic.
    d. anthelmintic.

81. A prescription is written for Septra® Suspension 240 ml 1 teaspoonful h.s. + 1 refill. The insurance plan has a 34-day supply limitation. How many ml can be dispensed using the insurance plan guidelines?
    a. 120 ml
    b. 170 ml
    c. 240 ml
    d. 360 ml

82. A prescription is written for Humulin® N U-100 insulin 10 ml, 40 units daily. What is the days supply?
    a. 25
    b. 34
    c. 21
    d. 28

83. A prescription is written for Tetracycline HCl suspension 125 mg/5 ml compounded from capsules and a mixture of Ora-Plus® 50% and Ora-Sweet® 50%. How many capsules of Tetracycline 250 mg are needed to prepare 50 ml of this suspension?
    a. 5
    b. 10
    c. 15
    d. 20

84. How many units of insulin does a 1/3 ml insulin syringe hold?
    a. 0.3
    b. 25
    c. 30
    d. 50

85. How many doses are in a 100 ml bottle of penicillin VK 250 mg/5 ml if each dose is 1/2 teaspoonful?
    a. 10
    b. 20
    c. 30
    d. 40

86. Which of the following medications is associated with gradual discontinuation of therapy?
    a. Amoxil®
    b. Sumycin®
    c. Medrol®
    d. Zovirax®

87. Alprozolam is a/an
    a. narcotic.
    b. barbiturate.
    c. benzodiazepine.
    d. stimulant.

Answers are on page 228.

88. A prescription for Duragesic® patches should be filed under which DEA schedule?
    a. Schedule I
    b. Schedule II
    c. Schedule III
    d. Schedule IV

89. Which of the following medications is an antidiarrheal?
    a. propranolol
    b. famotidine
    c. methylphenidate
    d. loperamide

90. If a medication is to be taken a.c., it should be taken
    a. in the morning.
    b. around the clock.
    c. after meals.
    d. before meals.

EXAM FOR THE CERTIFICATION OF PHARMACY TECHNICIANS (ExCPT)

PRACTICE EXAM

The following multiple choice questions are in the *choose the best answer* format of the national Exam for the Certification of Pharmacy Technicians (ExCPT) offered by the Institute for the Certification of Pharmacy Technicians (ICPT). There are four possible answers with only one answer being the most correct. Many of these questions can be answered through a careful review of this workbook. However, others require knowledge gained from practice as a technician. Answers for all questions can be found on page 228.

Since the time limit for taking the ExCPT is two hours, you may want to test your ability to answer the questions under a time limit, or you may simple wish to time yourself to see how long it takes you. There are 110 questions here, the same number as on the ExCPT exam. If you wish to have a similar experience, you can allow yourself two hours to answer these questions.

For more information on the Exam for the Certification of Pharmacy Technicians, see the preface of this Workbook.

Answers are on page 228.

1. 2000 ml of IV is to be delivered over 24 hours. What is the infusion rate in ml/hr?
   a. 1.4
   b. 2.8
   c. 83
   d. 140

2. A drug is teratogenic, therefore the drug should not be given to
   a. children.
   b. animals.
   c. pregnant women.
   d. elderly patients.

3. A patient brings in two new prescriptions from two different doctors. One prescription is for ibuprofen 800 mg, 1 tablet po t.i.d. and another prescription is for Anaprox DS®, 1 tablet b.i.d. What should the technician do?
   a. Tell the patient to decide which prescription s/he wants to fill.
   b. Tell the patient that s/he must get generic for both prescriptions.
   c. Alert the pharmacist of a possible therapeutic duplication.
   d. Fill both prescriptions as written.

4. A patient has a prescription on file for Cortisporin® Otic Suspension and brings in a new prescription that was issued today for Cortisporin® Otic Solution. What should the technician do?
   a. Fill the prescription for Cortisporin® Otic Suspension today because the refills will expire sooner.
   b. Fill the prescription for Cortisporin® Otic Solution today and alert the pharmacist that the other prescription is on file.
   c. Tell the patient to hold on to the prescription for Cortisporin® Otic Solution because the Cortisporin® Otic Suspension prescription has refills.
   d. Fill both prescriptions without consulting with the pharmacist.

5. A patient is allergic to aspirin. Which drug contains aspirin?
   a. Percocet®
   b. Tylox®
   c. Fiorinal®
   d. Ultracet®

6. A patient is allergic to penicillin. Which drug is most likely to cause an allergic reaction?
   a. Biaxin®
   b. Sumycin®
   c. Cleocin®
   d. Augmentin®

7. A small volume intravenous bag specifically used to deliver medication is called an
   a. LVP.
   b. IVPB.
   c. vial.
   d. ampule.

8. According to federal law, the prescriber must provide his/her DEA number for which of the following prescriptions?
   a. Ultram®
   b. Xanax®
   c. Elavil®
   d. Prozac®

9. Accutane® is associated with
   a. iPLEDGE.
   b. RevAssist.
   c. STEPS.
   d. TOUCH.

10. An ampule contains 500 mcg of digoxin in 2 ml. What volume is needed to deliver 0.125 mg of digoxin?
    a. 0.25 ml
    b. 0.5 ml
    c. 1 ml
    d. 1.5 ml

Answers are on page 228.

11. An antibiotic is prescribed 15 mg/kg twice a day by IV. What is the daily dose in mg for a child weighing 66 pounds?
   a. 225 mg
   b. 450 mg
   c. 675 mg
   d. 900 mg

12. An EpiPen® contains 0.3 mg/0.3 ml. What is the ratio strength of epinephrine?
   a. 1:10
   b. 1:100
   c. 1:1,000
   d. 1:10,000

13. An example of a major drug–drug interaction is
   a. warfarin-aspirin.
   b. hydrocodone-codeine.
   c. guaifenesin-pseudoephedrine.
   d. hydrochlorothiazide-triamterene.

14. The patient's _____ is necessary for billing a prescription.
   a. birth date
   b. medication history
   c. allergy information
   d. disease information

15. As you are putting away an order from a wholesaler, you notice one bottle is missing a label. The pharmacist tells you that the medication cannot be dispensed and must be returned to the wholesaler or destroyed. The drug cannot be dispensed because it is
   a. adulterated.
   b. misbranded.
   c. exempt.
   d. recycled.

16. Companies that administer drug benefit programs are called
   a. HMOs.
   b. PBMs.
   c. MACs.
   d. PPOs.

17. Copy 2 of DEA Form 222 is
   a. retained by the pharmacy.
   b. retained by the wholesaler.
   c. retained by the manufacturer.
   d. forwarded to the DEA.

18. Diazepam is available in which of the following dosage forms?
   a. 0.5 mg tablets
   b. 5 mg tablets
   c. 5 mg capsules
   d. 10 mg capsules

19. Each tablet of Claritin D® 12 hour contains 120 mg of pseudoephedrine sulfate. What is the maximum number of tablets that could be sold in a single transaction if the maximum amount per transaction of pseudoephedrine is 3.6 g?
   a. 15
   b. 20
   c. 30
   d. 36

20. Exempt narcotics are in DEA schedule
   a. II.
   b. III.
   c. IV.
   d. V.

21. Exempt narcotics are regulated for how many dosage units can be sold without a prescription in a _____ hour period.
   a. 24
   b. 48
   c. 72
   d. 168

22. Federal law requires pharmacies to keep _____ of the DEA Form 222.
   a. Copy 1
   b. Copy 2
   c. Copy 3
   d. Copy 4

Answers are on page 228.

23. For aseptic technique, all work should be performed at least _____ inches inside the hood.
    a. 2
    b. 4
    c. 6
    d. 8

24. For children 23–40 kg, the dose of Tamiflu® is 60 mg b.i.d. for 5 days and for children 15–23 kg, the dose is 45 mg b.i.d. for 5 days. What is the dose for a child weighing 38 lbs. if the strength is 12 mg/ml?
    a. 2.5 ml
    b. 3.75 ml
    c. 5 ml
    d. .5 ml

25. For the electrolyte KCl, Cl represents
    a. potassium.
    b. chloride.
    c. sodium.
    d. calcium.

26. For the following directions, how many drops per day will be administered?
    Timolol 0.25% 10 ml, Sig: gtts ii ou b.i.d.
    a. 2
    b. 4
    c. 8
    d. 12

27. For the following prescription, how much drug is taken each day?
    Amoxicillin 250 mg/5 ml 150 ml, Sig: 2 drams t.i.d.
    a. 15 ml
    b. 30 ml
    c. 45 ml
    d. 50 ml

28. Hemoglobin A1C is monitored for patients with
    a. diabetes.
    b. hypertension.
    c. epilepsy.
    d. bone marrow suppression.

29. How many 4 oz. bottles can be filled from a pint of cough syrup?
    a. 2
    b. 3
    c. 4
    d. 8

30. How many cases of 8 dram vials should be ordered to last two weeks if there are 500 vials per case and the pharmacy uses 120 vials per day on average?
    a. 2
    b. 4
    c. 6
    d. 8

31. How many grams of dextrose are in 20 ml of 70% dextrose solution?
    a. 7
    b. 14
    c. 70
    d. 140

32. How many grams of dextrose are in 400 ml of a solution of 70% dextrose?
    a. 2.8
    b. 28
    c. 280
    d. 2,800

33. How many grams of sucrose are needed to prepare 4 ounces of a 20% solution?
    a. 6
    b. 12
    c. 24
    d. 36

Answers are on page 228.

34. How many milliliters of magnesium sulfate 4 mEq/ml are needed to add 10 mEq of magnesium sulfate to an IV bag?
    a. 2
    b. 2.5
    c. 4
    d. 10

35. How much diluent should be added to 500 ml of 70% ethanol so the concentration is 50%?
    a. 100 ml
    b. 200 ml
    c. 300 ml
    d. 400 ml

36. How much hydrocortisone powder is needed to compound 60 g of hydrocortisone cream 2%?
    a. 1.2 mg
    b. 1,200 mg
    c. 0.06 g
    d. 6 g

37. How much medication should be dispensed for five days if the dose is 50 mg/kg/day and the patient weights 44 pounds if the medication is available 250 mg/5 ml and administered four times per day?
    a. 50 ml
    b. 100 ml
    c. 150 ml
    d. 200 ml

38. How much should be withdrawn from a vial if the strength of the medication is 0.5 mg/ml and a dose of 250 micrograms is needed?
    a. 0.25 ml
    b. 0.5 ml
    c. 1 ml
    d. 5 ml

39. How should a prescription for BenzaClin® be stored after it has been mixed?
    a. refrigerator
    b. freezer
    c. room temperature
    d. in a warm and moist environment as defined by USP

40. If a 1,000 ml IV bag is set to run at 60 ml/hour, what is the rate in ml/min?
    a. 0.5
    b. 1
    c. 2
    d. 3

41. If a medication is to be taken p.c., when should it be taken?
    a. after meals
    b. in the evening
    c. before meals
    d. in the morning

42. If an eye dropper delivers 20 drops per ml, how many days should a 5 ml prescription last if the dose is two drops in each eye four times a day?
    a. 6
    b. 12
    c. 18
    d. 24

43. If the dose of liquid amoxicillin for a child is one and one-half teaspoonfuls three times a day for 10 days, what is the volume needed to fill the prescription?
    a. 100 ml
    b. 150 ml
    c. 200 ml
    d. 225 ml

44. Information about generic equivalents can be found in the
    a. *Red Book.*
    b. "Orange Book."
    c. Blue Book.
    d. Green Book.

Answers on page 228.

45. KCl is administered in 1,000 ml of D5W at a rate of 125 ml/hour. How many hours will this IV last?
   a. 4
   b. 6
   c. 8
   d. 10

46. MedWatch Form 3500 is for reporting adverse reactions to
   a. vaccines.
   b. drugs.
   c. veterinary products.
   d. produce.

47. Normal saline solution is
   a. hypotonic.
   b. isotonic.
   c. hypertonic.
   d. hyperosmotic.

48. OSHA required notices for hazardous substances that provide hazard, handling, cleanup, and first aid information are called
   a. MAC.
   b. MSDS.
   c. MEC.
   d. HCFA-1500.

49. Pharmacy technicians may sell exempt narcotics
   a. after the pharmacist has approved and documented the sale in a bound record book.
   b. without approval from the pharmacist if they record the sale in a record book.
   c. as long as the purchaser is over 18 years old.
   d. without approval or documentation.

50. Plan B® has dual marketing status and can be sold without a prescription to individuals
   a. 16 years and older.
   b. 17 years and older.
   c. 18 years and older.
   d. 21 years and older.

51. Premarin® Cream has been prescribed 0.5 g pv twice a week. The medication should be administered
   a. vaginally.
   b. rectally.
   c. on the stomach.
   d. on the forearms.

52. Lidoderm® is an example of a/an
   a. analgesic.
   b. anti-anxiety.
   c. anesthetic.
   d. antidepressant.

53. What is the % concentration if 268 g of sugar is in 400 ml of aqueous solution?
   a. 33%
   b. 50%
   c. 67%
   d. 75%

54. Sublingual nitroglycerin is used for
   a. hyperlipidemia.
   b. angina.
   c. hypertension.
   d. coagulation.

55. The term for a drug that reduces fever is
   a. analgesic.
   b. antipyretic.
   c. anti-inflammatory.
   d. antidepressant.

56. The approximate metric volume of 8 oz. of liquid is
   a. 120 ml.
   b. 180 ml.
   c. 240 ml.
   d. 360 ml.

57. The brand name for lorazepam is
   a. Klonopin®.
   b. Tranxene®.
   c. Ativan®.
   d. Serax®.

Answers are on page 228.

58. The class of drugs to dissolve blood clots is
    a. thrombolytics.
    b. vasopressors.
    c. antianginals.
    d. antihypertensives

59. The CMEA sets _____ and _____ limits on the over-the-counter sale of pseudoephedrine.
    a. daily, weekly
    b. weekly, monthly
    c. daily, monthly
    d. monthly, yearly

60. The commission that surveys and accredits healthcare organizations is the
    a. DPH.
    b. FDA.
    c. ASHP.
    d. JCAHO.

61. The concentration of a drug is 300 mg/250 ml. In order to deliver 1 mg/minute, the IV should be set to deliver
    a. 25 ml/hr.
    b. 30 ml/hr.
    c. 50 ml/hr.
    d. 60 ml/hr.

62. The Controlled Substances Act is enforced by the
    a. FDA.
    b. CPSC.
    c. DEA.
    d. Bureau of Alcohol Tobacco and Firearms.

63. The directions state 2 gtt a.u. q 12 h. How is the drug to be administered?
    a. both ears
    b. right eye
    c. by mouth
    d. topically

64. The doctor orders 1/4 gr Codeine. How many milligrams is this?
    a. 15 mg
    b. 30 mg
    c. 60 mg
    d. 90 mg

65. The dose of a medication is 7.5 ml. How many teaspoonfuls is this dose?
    a. 0.5
    b. 1
    c. 1.5
    d. 2

66. The following drugs are antidepressants EXCEPT
    a. citalopram.
    b. trazodone.
    c. venlafaxine.
    d. diazepam.

67. The following drugs are considered antihyperlipidemic drugs EXCEPT
    a. Pravachol®.
    b. Tricor ®.
    c. Vytorin®.
    d. Aldactone®.

68. The following medications should be refrigerated EXCEPT
    a. Biaxin® suspension.
    b. Augmentin® suspension.
    c. Duricef® suspension.
    d. Thyrolar®.

69. The generic name for Neurontin® is
    a. gabapentin.
    b. etodolac.
    c. nabumetone.
    d. finasteride.

Answers are on page 228.

70. The government agency that regulates investigational medications is the
    a. FDA.
    b. DEA.
    c. CPSC.
    d. USP.

71. The infusion of an IV is over twelve hours. The total volume is 1,000 ml. What would the infusion rate be in mL per minute?
    a. 83.3 ml/minute
    b. 8.3 ml/minute
    c. 16.7 ml/minute
    d. 1.4 ml/minute

72. The middle set of digits of the NDC represents
    a. the manufacturer.
    b. product identification.
    c. package size.
    d. country of origin.

73. The mixing instructions for a liquid antibiotic call for 45 mL of water for constitution to make a 150 mL suspension. The final concentration of the suspension is 250 mg/5 mL. What is the powder volume?
    a. 45 mL
    b. 90 mL
    c. 105 mL
    d. 205 mL

74. The pharmacist should be alerted if a patient is allergic to sulfa and prescribed
    a. Ceftin®.
    b. Keflex®.
    c. Eryc®.
    d. Bactrim®.

75. The *Red Book* provides information about
    a. pricing.
    b. stability.
    c. solubility.
    d. generic substitution.

76. The Roman Numeral XIX is equivalent to
    a. 21.
    b. 14.
    c. 19.
    d. 29.

77. The temperature of a refrigerator in a pharmacy should generally be
    a. 33–45° F.
    b. 40–42° F.
    c. 43–55° F.
    d. 50–52° F.

78. The type of formulary that allows the pharmacy to obtain only drugs listed on the formulary with no exceptions is a/an
    a. open formulary.
    b. closed formulary.
    c. third party formulary.
    d. P&T list.

79. The type of medication order for medication to be administered only on an as needed basis is called a
    a. standing order.
    b. PRN order.
    c. STAT order.
    d. standard order.

80. The unique identifying number of a drug is called a/an
    a. NDC.
    b. PHI.
    c. NPI.
    d. DEA.

81. Theft or loss of controlled substances must be recorded on DEA Form
    a. 41.
    b. 106.
    c. 222.
    d. 224.

Answers are on page 228.

82. Two teaspoonfuls is equal to
    a. 5 ml.
    b. 8 ml.
    c. 10 ml.
    d. 16 ml.

83. The type of recall for drug products most likely to cause serious adverse effects or death is
    a. Class I.
    b. Class II.
    c. Class III.
    d. Class V.

84. Under HIPAA, who CANNOT have access to information about a patient's prescription?
    a. the patient
    b. the pharmacist & support staff
    c. the physician/prescriber and support staff
    d. the pharmaceutical companies or their representatives

85. Under the Combat Methamphetamine Epidemic Act, what is the maximum amount of pseudoephedrine that can be sold per month to an individual?
    a. 3.6 g
    b. 7.5 g
    c. 10 g
    d. 20 g

86. Warfarin is a common
    a. thrombolytic.
    b. anticoagulant.
    c. vasopressor.
    d. vasodilator.

87. What is the cost for 60 tablets of a drug if the cost for 100 tablets is $75.00?
    a. $39.30
    b. $43.66
    c. $45
    d. $48.46

88. What is the generic name for Elavil®?
    a. fluoxetine
    b. imipramine
    c. doxepin
    d. amitryptiline

89. What proportion of 20% alcohol should be mixed with 60% alcohol to prepare 40% alcohol?
    a. 1:1
    b. 1:2
    c. 2:1
    d. 1:4

90. What size insulin syringe is needed to deliver a dose of 60 units?
    a. 0.3 ml
    b. 0.5 ml
    c. 1 ml
    d. 2 ml

91. What type of insulin is a clear solution?
    a. NPH
    b. Lente
    c. Regular
    d. Ultralente

92. Which class of drugs is used to treated elevated blood lipids?
    a. keratolytics
    b. anthelmintics
    c. antihyperlipidemics
    d. antihistamines

93. Which DAW code should be entered if a physician has ordered Coumadin D.A.W.?
    a. 0
    b. 1
    c. 2
    d. 3

Answers are on page 228.

94. Which drug does not require child resistant packaging according to the Poison Prevention Packaging Act?
    a. nitroglycerin sublingual tablets
    b. isosorbide dinitrate oral tablets
    c. nitroglycerin sustained release capsules
    d. isosorbide mononitrate oral tablets

95. Which drug information resource is updated monthly?
    a. *Physicians' Desk Reference*
    b. *Drug Facts and Comparisons*
    c. *Martindale's*
    d. *Drug Information Handbook*

96. Which drug is an NSAID?
    a. bumetanide
    b. nabumetone
    c. doxazosin
    d. meclizine

97. Which information is not required by federal law on a prescription label?
    a. date
    b. patient's name
    c. prescriber's name
    d. national drug code

98. Which medication is ordered using DEA Form 222?
    a. alprazolam
    b. phenobarbital
    c. diazepam
    d. morphine sulfate

99. Which of the following drugs is a controlled substance?
    a. phenobarbital
    b. carbamazepine
    c. imipramine
    d. furosemide

100. Which of the following drugs is considered a diuretic?
    a. furosemide
    b. lovastatin
    c. hydroxyzine
    d. hydralazine

101. Which of the following drugs is considered an analgesic?
    a. tramadol
    b. phenelzine
    c. lidocaine
    d. diazepam

102. Which of the following drugs is NOT an antihistamine?
    a. diphenhydramine
    b. paroxetine
    c. desloratadine
    d. cetirizine

103. Which of the following medications does not require ordering with DEA Form 222?
    a. Percodan®.
    b. Percocet®.
    c. Codeine.
    d. Stadol®.

104. Which of the following vitamins is known as vitamin C?
    a. ascorbic acid
    b. cyanocobalamin
    c. ergocalciferol
    d. thiamine

105. While preparing a prescription, a bottle of finasteride is spilled on the floor and some tablets are broken. Who should stay away from the spill area?
    a. males with BPH
    b. females in menopause
    c. females who are or may become pregnant
    d. males with hypertension

ExCPT PRACTICE EXAM

Answers are on page 228.

106. Who is authorized to sign a DEA Form 222 order form?
    a. pharmacy technicians
    b. licensed pharmacists
    c. individuals with power of attorney
    d. pharmacy managers

107. You are preparing a prescription for Patanol®. Where in the pharmacy should you look for the drug?
    a. ophthalmics and otics
    b. tablets and capsules
    c. creams and ointments
    d. refrigerator

108. You are putting away an order from a wholesaler and notice the packages in one order crate are floating in water. The pharmacist tells you that the medications in that crate cannot be dispensed and must be destroyed or returned to the wholesaler. These drugs cannot be dispensed because they are
    a. adulterated.
    b. misbranded.
    c. exempt.
    d. recycled.

109. You have a prescription from a doctor with the professional designation of O.D. What is the doctor's area of practice?
    a. chiropractor
    b. eyes
    c. ears
    d. osteopathic medicine

110. Zostavax® should be stored at 5° F or colder. What temperature is this in degrees C?
    a. 0°
    b. -5°
    c. -10°
    d. -15°

ExCPT Practice Exam

Use this space to make notes of what you may still need to study after having scored your exam.

CALCULATIONS PRACTICE EXAM

The following multiple choice problems provide you with extra practice with pharmacy calculations before taking a national certification exam. There are four possible answers for each problem, with only one answer being the most correct. Similar to the questions in the certification exams, many of the problems in the Calculations Practice Exam can be solved using techniques that are included in this workbook; however, others require knowledge gained from practice as a technician. Answers for all questions can be found on page 228.

Pharmacy calculations must be carefully done with 100% accuracy. Therefore, you should practice doing calculations using a systematic approach for problem-solving and always double-check your work. This Calculations Practice Exam contains 50 problems that are designed to provide you with extra practice with pharmacy calculations before taking a certification exam.

Answers are on page 228.

1. You are filling a prescription that reads: Amoxicillin 125 mg/5 ml, Sig 1 tsp t.i.d. Dispense 150 ml. How many milliliters should the patient take each day?
   a. 5 ml
   b. 10 ml
   c. 15 ml
   d. 20 ml

2. You are filling a prescription that reads: EES® 200, Sig 1 tsp t.i.d. Dispense 150 ml. How many days should this prescription last?
   a. 5 days
   b. 7 days
   c. 10 days
   d. 14 days

3. A compounded prescription calls for 600 gm of white petrolatum. How many 1 lb jars should you obtain so there is enough to prepare this prescription?
   a. 1 jar
   b. 2 jars
   c. 3 jars
   d. 4 jars

4. Each tablet of Tylenol® #3 has 30 mg of codeine. How many grains of codeine are in each tablet of Tylenol® #3?
   a. 1/2 grain
   b. 1 grain
   c. 2 grains
   d. 3 grains

5. One form of influenza vaccine, the Live Attenuated Intranasal Vaccine, must be stored at -15° C. What is this temperature in degrees F?
   a. 5° F
   b. -5° F
   c. 27° F
   d. -27° F

6. The lead pharmacy technician must reorder billing forms when 80% of the case has been used. A full case of billing forms contains 20 packages of forms. How many packages of forms should be remaining in the case when it's time to reorder?
   a. 16 packages
   b. 12 packages
   c. 8 packages
   d. 4 packages

7. In reconstituting a liquid antibiotic, 90 ml of distilled water should be used. If 1/3 of the water should be added first to moisten the powder, how much water should be added to moisten the powder?
   a. 45 ml
   b. 60 ml
   c. 15 ml
   d. 30 ml

8. How many capsules of clindamycin hydrochloride should be used to prepare 30 ml of the following preparation, if each capsule contains 150 mg of clindamycin hydrochloride?

   clindamycin hydrochloride   600 mg
   70% isopropyl alcohol   qs ad 60 ml
   a. 4 capsules
   b. 2 capsules
   c. 10 capsules
   d. 20 capsules

9. A prescription is written for ibuprofen 10% cream. How much ibuprofen is needed to make 20 gm of the cream?
   a. 400 mg
   b. 200 mg
   c. 2 gm
   d. 4 gm

CALCULATIONS PRACTICE EXAM

Answers are on page 228.

10. You are entering a prescription for an albuterol inhaler that delivers 90 mcg per actuation. If each container delivers 200 actuations and each dose is two actuations, how many mg are delivered in each dose?
    a. 180 mg
    b. 90 mg
    c. 0.18 mg
    d. 0.09 mg

11. What is the days supply for a Z-Pak® that contains six azithromycin 250 mg tablets, with directions of 500 mg on the first day, followed by 250 mg once daily until gone?
    a. 3
    b. 5
    c. 4
    d. 6

12. What is the day's supply for metronidazole vaginal gel 70 g, Sig 5 g twice daily?
    a. 5 days
    b. 7 days
    c. 10 days
    d. 14 days

13. What is the days supply for Humulin® N insulin 20 ml, if the dose is 40 U daily?
    a. 100 days
    b. 30 days
    c. 60 days
    d. 50 days

14. How much change should be given to a patient who gives you $50 to pay for 3 prescriptions if the patient's prescription plan has a $10 co-pay?
    a. $20
    b. $10
    c. $40
    d. $30

15. What is the gross profit for a prescription if the selling price is $73.14, the acquisition cost is $52.10, and the AWP is $65.12?
    a. $21.04
    b. $8.02
    c. $13.02
    d. $73.14

16. A prescription has been written for Prevacid® 30 mg #100, Sig i cap qd, 2 refills; however, the patient's insurance benefit has a 34-day supply limit. If the original prescription is filled for 34 capsules, how many refills of 34 would be available?
    a. 6 refills of 34
    b. 8 refills of 34
    c. 5 refills of 34
    d. 7 refills of 34

17. You are preparing a prescription for Synthroid® 0.1 mg tablets. How many micrograms are in each tablet?
    a. 0.1 mg
    b. 0.1 mcg
    c. 100 mg
    d. 100 mcg

18. You are entering a prescription for timolol 0.25% ophthalmic solution 5 ml, Sig i gtt o.u. twice daily. How many days should this bottle last if the dropper delivers 20 drops of timolol 0.25% ophthalmic solution per ml?
    a. 10 days
    b. 50 days
    c. 12.5 days
    d. 25 days

19. The dose of a drug is 250 micrograms per kg of body weight. What dose should be given to a child that weighs 55 lbs?
    a. 6.25 micrograms
    b. 6.25 mg
    c. 12.5 mg
    d. 12.5 micrograms

Answers are on page 228.

20. A physician has ordered 15 ml of Brand X Antacid Suspension to be taken four times daily. How many days will a 12 oz. bottle last?
    a. 6 days
    b. 12 days
    c. 3 days
    d. 10 days

21. How many mcg of digoxin are in 0.4 ml of digoxin solution if the strength of the digoxin solution is 50 mcg per ml?
    a. 20 mcg
    b. 125 mcg
    c. 0.02 mcg
    d. 12.5 mcg

22. You are filling a prescription for gentamicin 80 mg. How much gentamicin solution should be measured from a 2 ml vial of gentamicin 40 mg/ml?
    a. 2 ml
    b. 1 ml
    c. 0.8 ml
    d. 1.6 ml

23. 45 units of Humulin® R insulin are to be added to a TPN bag. How much Humulin R (U-100) is needed?
    a. 45 microliters
    b. 0.45 ml
    c. 4.5 ml
    d. 0.45 microliters

24. How much potassium chloride solution (2 mEq/ml) should be added to a 1 liter IV bag if 25 mEq of potassium chloride is needed?
    a. 25 ml
    b. 0.25 ml
    c. 12.5 ml
    d. 50 ml

25. How much sodium chloride is in 25 ml of normal saline?
    a. 225 g
    b. 225 mcg
    c. 225 mg
    d. 2.25 g

26. A drug is in a vial that contains 500 mg of the drug in 2 ml of solution. What is the percent strength of this drug?
    a. 2.5%
    b. 25%
    c. 10%
    d. 5%

27. You have dissolved 20 g of drug in 500 ml of solution. What is the percent strength of the resulting solution?
    a. 0.4%
    b. 4%
    c. 0.2%
    d. 2%

28. How many capsules are needed to prepare 30 ml of 1% clindamycin hydrochloride solution if each capsule contains 150 mg of clindamycin hydrochloride?
    a. 4 capsules
    b. 3 capsules
    c. 1 capsule
    d. 2 capsules

29. How much 1% lidocaine is needed to fill an order for 30 mg of lidocaine?
    a. 0.3 ml
    b. 3 ml
    c. 3 microliters
    d. 0.03 ml

30. What is the percent strength of a 1:100 solution?
    a. 10%
    b. 1%
    c. 0.01%
    d. 0.1%

CALCULATIONS PRACTICE EXAM

Answers are on page 228.

31. How much gentian violet is needed to pre-pare 100 ml of a 1:10,000 solution of gentian violet?
    a. 0.01 mg
    b. 10 g
    c. 10 mg
    d. 10 mcg

32. How much vancomycin should be given per dose for a child that weighs 32 lbs if the dose is 10 mg/kg q 6 h IV?
    a. 582 mg
    b. 145 mg
    c. 0.69 mg
    d. 704 mg

33. A patient is to receive 100 mg/kg/day of ampicillin. What is the total daily dose for a patient that weighs 40 lbs?
    a. 182 mg
    b. 1.8 g
    c. 18.2 g
    d. 0.182 g

34. If 250 mg of penicillin VK is equivalent to 400,000 Units of penicillin, how many Units of penicillin are in 1 mg of penicillin VK?
    a. 1,600 U
    b. 1,600 MU
    c. 16 MU
    d. 1.6 U

35. A nomogram has been used to determine a patient's BSA is 1.95. If the dose of a drug is 40 mg/sq. meter, how much drug should be administered per dose?
    a. 780 mg
    b. 7.8 g
    c. 78 mg
    d. 7.8 mg

36. A 500 ml IV bag is administered over 4 hours. What is the infusion rate?
    a. 125 ml/min
    b. 100 ml/min
    c. 100 ml/hr
    d. 125 ml/hr

37. A 500 ml IV bag is infused at a rate of 100 ml/hr. How long will this bag last?
    a. 2.5 hours
    b. 2 hours
    c. 10 hours
    d. 5 hours

38. An IV has been running at 80 ml/hr for 5 hours and 20 minutes. How much solution has the patient received?
    a. 427 ml
    b. 40 ml
    c. 400 ml
    d. 43 ml

39. An IV is set to deliver 30 drops/min. What is the infusion rate in ml/hr if there are 15 drops/ml?
    a. 30 ml/hr
    b. 40 ml/hr
    c. 120 ml/hr
    d. 270 ml/hr

40. How many ml of a 20% solution should be added to 50 ml of a 40% solution to obtain a 25% solution?
    a. 50 ml
    b. 100 ml
    c. 150 ml
    d. 200 ml

41. How many teaspoons equal 20 ml?
    a. 5
    b. 6
    c. 4
    d. 2

Answers are on page 228.

42. If a prescription reads: Aspirin 5gr, dispense 100 tablets, 1 tablet q 4-6h prn headache, what is the dose in milligrams?
    a. 650
    b. 750
    c. 100
    d. 325

43. How many gallons of Coca Cola™ fountain syrup are needed to package 150 bottles of 120 ml per bottle?
    a. 3
    b. 4
    c. 5
    d. 6

44. If a prescription reads: Amoxicillin 250 mg/5 ml, dispense 150 ml, 375 mg t.i.d. x 5d, what is the dose in household units?
    a. 1 teaspoonful
    b. 1 tablespoonful
    c. 1.5 teaspoonful
    d. 1.5 tablespoonful

45. How many ml are in 2 liters of normal saline?
    a. 200
    b. 2,000
    c. 0.2
    d. 0.002

46. How many ml of KCl 2 mEq/ml are needed if the dose is 30 mEq?
    a. 5
    b. 10
    c. 15
    d. 30

47. How many ml of 25% dextrose are needed to prepare 500 ml of 40% dextrose if you are to prepare 40% dextrose from 25% dextrose and 60% dextrose?
    a. 214 ml
    b. 286 ml
    c. 200 ml
    d. 300 ml

48. If 1 liter is infused over 8 hours, what is the rate of infusion in ml/hr?
    a. 62.5
    b. 100
    c. 125
    d. 250

49. A patient weighs 121 pounds. What is the patient's weight in kg?
    a. 37
    b. 45
    c. 55
    d. 68

50. How many grams of sodium bicarbonate are needed to make 400 ml of a 1:1000 w/v solution?
    a. 0.2
    b. 0.4
    c. 0.8
    d. 1

ANSWERS TO PRACTICE EXAMS

PTCE PRACTICE EXAM

1.	b
2.	d
3.	a
4.	a
5.	b
6.	b
7.	b
8.	c
9.	a
10.	c
11.	c
12.	d
13.	d
14.	b
15.	c
16.	a
17.	d
18.	c
19.	d
20.	b
21.	a
22.	d
23.	c
24.	b
25.	c
26.	a
27.	c
28.	c
29.	c
30.	c
31.	a
32.	c
33.	a
34.	d
35.	b
36.	a
37.	a
38.	c
39.	b
40.	c
41.	b
42.	a
43.	c
44.	b
45.	c
46.	b
47.	c
48.	b
49.	c
50.	c
51.	b
52.	b
53.	a
54.	b
55.	b
56.	c
57.	c
58.	d
59.	c
60.	b
61.	d
62.	d
63.	c
64.	a
65.	b
66.	b
67.	c
68.	c
69.	c
70.	b
71.	d
72.	b
73.	d
74.	c
75.	a
76.	a
77.	b
78.	b
79.	d
80.	a
81.	b
82.	a
83.	a
84.	c
85.	d
86.	c
87.	c
88.	b
89.	d
90.	d

ExCPT PRACTICE EXAM

1.	c
2.	c
3.	c
4.	b
5.	c
6.	d
7.	b
8.	b
9.	a
10.	b
11.	d
12.	c
13.	a
14.	a
15.	b
16.	b
17.	d
18.	b
19.	c
20.	d
21.	b
22.	c
23.	c
24.	b
25.	b
26.	c
27.	b
28.	a
29.	c
30.	b
31.	b
32.	c
33.	c
34.	b
35.	b
36.	b
37.	b
38.	b
39.	c
40.	b
41.	a
42.	a
43.	d
44.	b
45.	c
46.	b
47.	b
48.	b
49.	a
50.	b
51.	a
52.	c
53.	c
54.	b
55.	b
56.	c
57.	c
58.	a
59.	c
60.	d
61.	c
62.	c
63.	a
64.	a
65.	c
66.	d
67.	d
68.	a
69.	a
70.	a
71.	d
72.	b
73.	c
74.	d
75.	a
76.	c
77.	b
78.	b
79.	b
80.	a
81.	b
82.	c
83.	a
84.	d
85.	b
86.	b
87.	c
88.	d
89.	a
90.	c
91.	c
92.	c
93.	b
94.	a
95.	b
96.	b
97.	d
98.	d
99.	a
100.	a
101.	a
102.	b
103.	d
104.	a
105.	c
106.	c
107.	a
108.	a
109.	b
110.	d

CALCULATIONS PRACTICE EXAM

1.	c
2.	c
3.	b
4.	a
5.	a
6.	d
7.	d
8.	b
9.	c
10.	c
11.	b
12.	b
13.	d
14.	a
15.	a
16.	d
17.	d
18.	d
19.	b
20.	a
21.	a
22.	a
23.	b
24.	c
25.	c
26.	b
27.	b
28.	d
29.	b
30.	b
31.	c
32.	b
33.	b
34.	a
35.	c
36.	d
37.	d
38.	a
39.	c
40.	c
41.	c
42.	d
43.	c
44.	c
45.	b
46.	c
47.	b
48.	c
49.	c
50.	b

ANSWERS TO CHAPTER EXERCISES AND PROBLEMS

CHAPTER 1

p.4
1. cocaine
2. salicylic acid
3. quinine
4. pharmaceutical
5. panacea
6. pharmacology
7. penicillin
8. data
9. antitoxin
10. antibiotic
11. hormones
12. pharmacognosy
13. OBRA '90
14. formularies
15. managed care

p.5
1. F
2. T
3. T
4. F
5. T
6. T
7. F
8. F
9. T
10. F

p.6
1. c
2. d
3. b
4. a
5. c
6. d
7. b
8. a
9. b
10. c

CHAPTER 2

p.15
1. scope of practice
2. personal inventory
3. confidentiality
4. patient welfare
5. competent
6. certification
7. technicians
8. professionals
9. pharmacist
10. performance review
11. ASHP
12. detail oriented
13. continuing education
14. probation period

p.16
1. T
2. F
3. F
4. T
5. T
6. F
7. F
8. T
9. T
10. F

p.17
1. b
2. d
3. c
4. a
5. b
6. d
7. c
8. b
9. c
10. c

CHAPTER 3

p.23
1. DEA number
2. injunction
3. placebo
4. adverse effect
5. legend drug
6. negligence
7. pediatric
8. product labeling
9. "look-alike" regulation

ANSWERS TO CHAPTER EXERCISES AND PROBLEMS

10. liability
11. recall
12. controlled substance mark
13. NDC
14. exempt narcotics

p.24
1. F
2. T
3. T
4. T
5. T
6. F
7. T
8. T
9. F
10. T

p.25
1. Schedule II
2. Schedule III
3. Class III recall
4. Schedule V
5. Class II recall
6. Schedule I
7. Schedule IV
8. Class I recall

p.26
1. tight, light resistant
2. Endo Laboratories
3. Endocet®
4. oxycodone and acetaminophen
5. tablets
6. oxycodone hydrochloride and acetaminophen
7. C-II
8. room temperature
9. 06/2011

p.27
1. d
2. a
3. d
4. b
5. c
6. b
7. d

8. c
9. d
10. a

CHAPTER 4

p. 35
1. hypertension
2. fibromyalgia
3. encephalitis
4. meningitis
5. cardiomyopathy
6. endocrine
7. arthritis
8. hyperglycemia
9. mastitis
10. anorexia
11. colitis
12. hepatitis
13. gastritis
14. dysuria
15. subcutaneous
16. transdermal
17. hematoma
18. hemophilia
19. lymphoma
20. anuria
21. tendinitis
22. neuralgia
23. onchomycosis
24. endometriosis
25. vasectomy
26. prostatolith
27. bronchitis
28. pulmonary
29. cystitis
30. tympanitis
31. blepharitis

p.36
1. a
2. b
3. c
4. d
5. c
6. d
7. b

Answers to Chapter Exercises and Problems

8. c
9. c
10. b
11. c
12. a
13. b

Chapter 5

p.41
1. of each
2. before meals
3. right ear
4. morning
5. left ear
6. each ear
7. water
8. body surface area
9. twice a day
10. with
11. capsules
12. per gastric button
13. dilute
14. dispense
15. per nasogastric tube
16. dextrose 5% in water
17. elixir
18. fluid
19. gram
20. drop
21. hour
22. at bedtime
23. intramuscular
24. intravenous
25. intravenous push
26. no refill
27. intravenous piggyback
28. liter
29. left
30. liquid
31. microgram
32. milliequivalent
33. milligram
34. milliliter
35. no refill
36. normal saline
37. right eye
38. left eye
39. each eye

40. after meals
41. by nebulizer
42. by mouth
43. as needed
44. each, every
45. every day
46. every 6 hours
47. four times a day
48. a sufficient quantity
49. add sufficient quantity to make
50. without
51. subcutaneously
52. one-half
53. write, label
54. immediately
55. suppository
56. syrup
57. three times a day
58. tablets
59. tablespoon
60. topically
61. teaspoon
62. ointment
63. as directed

p.44
Prozac® Prescription
1. Prozac®
2. 20 mg
3. capsules
4. by mouth
5. one capsule every day
6. 2
7. no
Kenalog® Prescription
1. 0.1%
2. twice daily

p.45
Protonix® Prescription
1. 30
2. 1
Atrovent® HFA/Flovent® HFA Prescription
1. Each inhaler would last 33 days if two puffs per dose are used or 22 days if three puffs per dose are used. We would normally enter 22 days for the days supply on a prescription of this type.
2. 30 days

ANSWERS TO CHAPTER EXERCISES AND PROBLEMS

p.46
Synthroid® Prescription
1. DAW
Miacalcin® Prescription
1. Miacalcin® is a nasal spray. The directions read "one inhalation every day" and the patient should administer the medication to alternate nostrils, meaning that the patient should not use the same nostril two days in a row.

p.47
Metrogel® Prescription
1. A 70 gram tube should be dispensed
2. "per vagina"
Premarin®/Provera® Prescription
1. Since the patient takes the medication for 21 days and off for 7 days, the medication will last 28 days.
2. Since the patient takes the medication for only 5 days in a 28-day cycle, this medication will also last 28 days.

p.48
Ortho Novum® 777 Prescription
1. 7 (1 original fill plus 6 refills)
Bactrim® DS Prescription
1. sulfa allergy

p.49
Lorabid® Prescription
1. Take one teaspoonful twice daily for 10 days.
Amoxicillin, Biaxin®, and Aciphex® Prescriptions
1. 28
2. 14
3. 14

p.50
1. pneumonia, dehydration
2. penicillin allergy
3. every four hours by mouth
4. 2200 and 600 orders
5. 500 mg by mouth, every 12 hours
6. by mouth, each day

p.51
1. Lopressor® 50 mg, Hydrochlorothiazide 25 mg, and Sonata® 5 mg
2. one at bedtime as needed

p.52
Mary Smith Physician Order
1. docusate sodium 100 mg
2. Metamucil®
Andrew Smith Physician Order
1. This medication should be administered as soon as possible.
2. intramuscular injection

p.53
Steve Smith Physician Order
1. 100 cc per hour
2. hydrochlorothizide 25 mg and Diovan® 80 mg
Barbara Smith Physician Order
1. Micronase® 5 mg and Ambien® 5 mg
2. Ambien® 5 mg

p.54
1. prescription
2. extemporaneous compounding
3. HIPAA
4. signa
5. auxiliary label
6. medication order
7. look-alikes
8. Rx
9. DAW
10. PHI
11. institutional labels
12. DUR
13. NPI
14. DEA number

p.55
1. T
2. T
3. F
4. T
5. F
6. T
7. T
8. F
9. F
10. F

p.56
1. c
2. b

ANSWERS TO CHAPTER EXERCISES AND PROBLEMS

3. a
4. b
5. b
6. a
7. c
8. c
9. c
10. c
11. c
12. a
13. b
14. a
15. c

CHAPTER 6

p.60
1. 0.625
2. 0.002
3. 0.25
4. 0.67
5. 0.12
6. 0.425
7. 0.032
8. 70%
9. 75%
10. 150%
11. 12.5%
12. 7.5%
13. 80%
14. 2.5%
15. VII
16. XXIX
17. LXXI
18. CVIII
19. VIII
20. XCVIII
21. IX
22. 19
23. 103
24. 1900
25. 2 1/2
26. 30
27. 54

p.61, 64-65
1. 40
2. 42
3. 3.5

4. 2400 mg
5. 300 ml
6. 20 ml
7. 400 ml
8. 7.2 ml
9. 1 ml/min
10. 1.4
11. 360 ml
12. 357 ml of 70% dextrose and 643 ml of sterile water
13. 286 ml 70% dextrose and 714 ml sterile water
14. 250 ml 50% dextrose and 250 ml sterile water

p. 68
1. Aminosyn® 500 ml
2. dextrose   400 ml
3. KCl   12 ml
4. MVI   5 ml
5. NaCl   5.45 ml
6. sterile water   77.55 ml

CHAPTER 7

p.71
1. F
2. T
3. F
4. T
5. F
6. T
7. T
8. T
9. T
10. T

p.72
1. local effect
2. systemic effect
3. buffer system
4. bulk powders
5. buccal cavity
6. inactive ingredients
7. enteric coated
8. water soluble
9. sublingual administration
10. pH
11. parenteral

ANSWERS TO CHAPTER EXERCISES AND PROBLEMS

12. necrosis
13. ophthalmic
14. intradermal injections
15. intravenous sites
16. hemorrhoid
17. solvent
18. lacrimal canalicula
19. transcorneal transport
20. emulsion
21. intramuscular injection sites
22. subcutaneous injection sites
23. viscosity
24. alveoli
25. wheal
26. lacrimal gland
27. elastomeric pump
28. conjunctiva
29. Z-tract injection
30. nasal mucosa
31. atomizer
32. nasal inhaler
33. inspiration
34. metered dose inhalers
35. percutaneous
36. elixirs
37. syrups
38. sterile
39. Toxic Shock Syndrome
40. contraceptive
41. IUD

p.74
1. intraocular
2. intranasal
3. sublingual or oral
4. inhalation
5. peroral
6. intravenous
7. vaginal
8. subcutaneous
9. intramuscular

p. 75, Routes of Administration
1. intradermal
2. subcutaneous
3. intravenous
4. intramuscular
Intramuscular Administration Sites
1. a

2. d
3. b
4. e
5. c

p.76
1. c
2. a
3. b
4. c
5. c
6. b
7. b
8. a
9. a
10. c
11. a
12. d
13. a
14. d

CHAPTER 8

p.81
1. F
2. T
3. T
4. F
5. T
6. F

p.88
1. aseptic techniques
2. pyrogens
3. Flashball
4. isotonic
5. hypertonic
6. hypotonic
7. flow rate
8. heparin lock
9. piggybacks
10. chemical complexation
11. admixture
12. lyophilized
13. diluent
14. ready-to-mix systems
15. bevel
16. gauge
17. lumen

ANSWERS TO CHAPTER EXERCISES AND PROBLEMS

18. coring
19. membrane filter
20. depth filter
21. final filter
22. laminar flow
23. HEPA filter
24. biological safety cabinets
25. irrigation solution
26. ampules
27. sharps
28. additive
29. RCRA
30. valence
31. LVP solution
32. SVP solution
33. TPN solution
34. TNA solution
35. dialysis

p.90
1.   b
2.   c
3.   a
4.   c
5.   c
6.   d
7.   b
8.   c
9.   a
10. b
11. d
12. a
13. d
14. b
15. c
16. c

CHAPTER 9

p.97
1.   F
2.   T
3.   T
4.   T
5.   T
6.   F
7.   F
8.   F
9.   F

10. T
11. F
12. T

p.102
1.   extemporaneous compounding
2.   USP/NF Chapter <795>
3.   USP/NF Chapter <797>
4.   calibrate
5.   volumetric
6.   arrest knob
7.   meniscus
8.   trituration
9.   levigation
10. geometric dilution
11. sonication
12. spatulation
13. formulation record
14. aliquot
15. syrup
16. sensitivity
17. flocculating agents
18. thickening agent
19. USP/NF grade
20. primary standard
21. emulsifier
22. emulsion
23. water-in-oil
24. oil-in-water
25. hydrophilic emulsifier
26. lipophilic emulsifier
27. primary emulsion
28. mucilage
29. compression molding
30. fusion molding
31. "punch" method

p.104
1.   a
2.   b
3.   a
4.   c
5.   b
6.   d
7.   b
8.   b
9.   a
10. a
11. a
12. d

Answers to Chapter Exercises and Problems

13. a
14. b
15. b
16. c

Chapter 10

p.112
1. biopharmaceutics
2. site of action
3. receptor
4. selective action
5. agonists
6. antagonists
7. minimum effective concentration
8. onset of action
9. therapeutic window
10. disposition
11. passive diffusion
12. active transport
13. hydrophobic
14. hydrophilic
15. lipoidal
16. gastric emptying time
17. complex
18. protein binding
19. metabolite
20. enzyme
21. enzyme induction
22. enzyme inhibition
23. first pass metabolism
24. enterohepatic cycling
25. nephron
26. glomerular filtration
27. bioavailability
28. bioequivalency
29. pharmaceutical equivalents
30. pharmaceutical alternatives
31. therapeutic equivalents

p.114
1. T
2. T
3. T
4. F
5. F
6. T
7. T
8. F

9. F
10. T
11. F

p.114
1. b
2. a
3. c
4. b
5. a
6. a
7. c
8. d
9. b
10. d
11. a
12. c
13. a
14. c

Chapter 11

p.118
1. hypersensitivity
2. anaphylactic shock
3. idiosyncrasy
4. hepatotoxicity
5. nephrotoxicity
6. carcinogenicity
7. teratogenicity
8. additive effects
9. synergism
10. enzyme inhibition
11. displacement
12. child
13. neonate
14. hypothyroidism
15. hyperthyroidism
16. adolescent
17. cirrhosis
18. infant

p.119
1. F
2. T
3. T
4. T
5. T
6. F

Answers to Chapter Exercises and Problems

7. T
8. T
9. T
10. T

p.120
1. d
2. b
3. c
4. c
5. c
6. d
7. a
8. d
9. a
10. b
11. a
12. b
13. b

Chapter 12

p.124
1. primary literature
2. tertiary literature
3. *Red Book*
4. Material Safety Data Sheets (MSDS)
5. secondary literature
6. *AHFS Drug Information*
7. *Drug Facts and Comparisons*
8. *Physician's Desk Reference*
9. *Handbook on Injectable Drugs*
10. World Wide Web
11. Martindale
12. browser
13. Internet Service Provider
14. URL

p.125
1. T
2. T
3. T
4. F
5. F
6. T
7. T
8. T
9. F
10. T
11. T

p.126
1. c
2. b
3. d
4. d
5. c
6. a
7. d
8. a
9. a
10. c
11. b
12. c
13. a
14. d

Chapter 13

p.130
1. open formulary
2. closed formulary
3. turnover
4. Schedule II substances
5. perpetual inventory
6. inventory
7. reorder points
8. order entry device
9. therapeutic equivalent
10. purchase order number
11. automated dispensing system
12. unit-dose
13. dispensing units

p.131
1. T
2. F
3. T
4. F
5. T
6. F
7. T
8. F
9. F
10. T

p.132
1. b
2. d
3. b

Answers to Chapter Exercises and Problems

4. a
5. b
6. a
7. c
8. d
9. d
10. b

Chapter 14

p.136
1. pharmacy benefit managers
2. online adjudication
3. co-insurance
4. co-pay
5. dual co-pay
6. maximum allowable cost
7. U&C or UCR
8. HMO
9. POS
10. PPO
11. deductible
12. prescription drug benefit cards
13. CPT code
14. Medicare
15. Medicaid
16. CMS 1500 form (formerly HCFA 1500)
17. workers' compensation
18. patient assistance programs
19. universal claim form

p.137
1. F
2. T
3. T
4. T
5. T
6. T
7. F
8. T

p.138
1. b
2. a
3. d
4. b
5. d
6. d
7. d

8. c
9. b
10. a

Chapter 15

p.144
1. OBRA
2. interpersonal skills
3. scope of practice
4. transaction windows
5. refrigeration
6. patient identification number
7. group number
8. signature log
9. HIPAA
10. safety caps
11. counting tray
12. shelf stickers
13. Disease State Management Services
14. auxiliary labels
15. unit price

p.145
1. T
2. T
3. T
4. F
5. F
6. T
7. T
8. T
9. T
10. F
11. T

p.146
1. b
2. a
3. a
4. c
5. a
6. a
7. c
8. c
9. b
10. a

ANSWERS TO CHAPTER EXERCISES AND PROBLEMS

CHAPTER 16

p.156
1. reconstitute
2. demographics
3. electronic medical record
4. unit dose
5. standing order
6. PRN order
7. STAT order
8. medication administration record (MAR)
9. code cart
10. central pharmacy
11. inpatient pharmacy
12. pharmacy satellite
13. pneumatic tube system
14. clean rooms
15. outpatient pharmacy
16. policy and procedure manual
17. final filter

p.157
1. F
2. F
3. T
4. T
5. F
6. T
7. T

p.158
1. b
2. b
3. d
4. a
5. d
6. a
7. d
8. c
9. c
10. b
11. b
12. b

CHAPTER 17

p.161
1. F
2. T
3. F

4. T
5. F
6. F
7. T
8. T

p.162
1. d
2. d
3. d
4. a
5. a
6. c
7. d
8. c
9. a
10. b

CHAPTER 18

p.172
1. Respiratory Agent
2. Psychotropic Agent
3. Cardiovascular Agent
4. Anti-infective
5. Anti-infective
6. Cardiovascular Agent
7. Cardiovascular Agent
8. Anti-infective
9. Musculoskeletal Agent
10. Cardiovascular Agent
11. Anti-infective
12. Respiratory Agent
13. Anti-infective
14. Psychotropic agent
15. Anti-infective
16. Cardiovascular Agent
17. Dermatological Agent
18. Cardiovascular Agent
19. Gastrointestinal Agent
20. Cardiovascular Agent
21. Psychotropic Agent
22. Anti-infective Agent
23. Respiratory Agent
24. Cardiovascular Agent
25. Antidiabetic
26. Cardiovascular Agent
27. Dermatological Agent
28. Analgesic

ANSWERS TO CHAPTER EXERCISES AND PROBLEMS

29. Antidiabetic Agent
30. Gastrointestinal Agent
31. Anti-infective Agent
32. Cardiovascular Agent
33. Gastrointestinal Agent
34. Cardiovascular Agent
35. Cardiovascular Agent
36. Cardiovascular Agent
37. Gastrointestinal Agent
38. Gastrointestinal Agent
39. Electrolytic Agent
40. Analgesic
41. Psychotropic Agent
42. Dermatological Agent
43. Electrolytic Agent
44. Antineoplastic
45. Analgesic
46. Gastrointestinal Agent
47. Anti-infective
48. Cardiovascular Agent

p.174
Analgesics
1. h
2. a
3. g
4. b
5. c
6. f
7. d
8. e
Anti-infectives
1. d
2. c
3. b
4. h
5. g
6. a
7. e
8. f
Cardiovascular Agents
1. a
2. e
3. f
4. b
5. h
6. d
7. c
8. g

p.175
Dermatologicals
1. f
2. h
3. g
4. a
5. c
6. b
7. d
8. e
Gastrointestinal Agents
1. c
2. d
3. g
4. a
5. e
6. h
7. f
8. b

p.176
Hormones & Modifiers: Adrenal corticosteroids
1. a
2. b
3. c
4. d
Hormones & Modifiers: Oral antidiabetics
1. e
2. c
3. b
4. d
5. a
Musculoskeletal Agents
1. b
2. c
3. f
4. d
5. e
6. a
Neurological Agents
1. g
2. e
3. b
4. c
5. a
6. h
7. d
8. f

ANSWERS TO CHAPTER EXERCISES AND PROBLEMS

p.177
Psychotropic Agents
1. a
2. f
3. e
4. g
5. b
6. h
7. d
8. c

Respiratory Agents
1. b
2. d
3. f
4. e
5. c
6. g
7. a

p.178
1. T
2. F
3. F
4. T
5. F
6. T
7. F
8. F
9. T
10. F

1. c
2. d
3. a
4. b
5. b
6. a
7. c
8. c
9. b
10. b
11. a
12. b
13. a
14. c
15. a

KEY CONCEPTS INDEX

KEY CONCEPTS INDEX